GREATNESS PASSING BY

GREATNESS PASSING BY

STORIES TO TELL TO BOYS AND GIRLS

By

HULDA NIEBUHR

CHARLES SCRIBNER'S SONS
NEW YORK · LONDON
1943

TO THE
CHILDREN OF BETHEL
AND TO
CYNTHIA

"When the high heart we magnify,
And the sure vision celebrate,
And worship greatness passing by,
Ourselves are great."

JOHN DRINKWATER.

CONTENTS

CONTENTS

PREFACE

IN DEFENSE OF STORIES

In the olden, that is the more or less olden days of
very formal teaching, the story held a central place in
the moral and religious education of children. It
was often a dogmatic story, told to give a definite
pattern of action, or to state some debatable truth in
terms of incontrovertible fact. Sometimes it was a
sentimental story through which the teller sought to
stamp his appreciations upon the hearers whether or
no. When the pupil "knew" the story the educational process was complete so far as the teacher was
concerned.

In the reaction against a teaching method in
which it had been the misused tool, the story has
changed in form and use but it has not lost its important place. Any educational approach which presumes to relate itself to life will use the story, for the
story has its roots in life, it is life condensed, life in
spot-light, it is of the essence of life itself.

The universal interest in stories, the fact that all

ages and all conditions of folk enjoy the story, is due largely to the fact that the story makes its listeners and readers into creators. Its appeal is great because it gives the listener, or the reader, the heightened sense of living which always accompanies a creative activity. The magic of the story's words causes the imagination of each hearer to work in an original, creative fashion even though the general pattern is indicated, for each imagination paints its screen with the pigments and shapes of its own interpretation, out of its own background of experience.

Although they come out of the background of personal experience these pictures constitute a new world. They open the door to new experience. The story takes the hearer out of his present-day world into a new realm of new associations and sets him watching in curiosity for the next development. That is an added reason why the story heightens the tempo of life. It introduces new vistas, new experiences, which increase the scope of life.

When imagination is active in this way the hearer does not merely see things happen,—he feels them happen. He shares in the emotions of the characters in the story and takes an attitude in relation to them and to the outcome of the story. There is no cool knowing and perceiving, but "we feel that which we perceive and imagine that which we know."

This appeal in the story to emotion and imagination, this calling forth of the hearer to be identified with the story characters, constitutes a strong asset for education. The story of Abraham Lincoln, tired, trudging the country road after the day's work in the store, to return some money in his possession because he had made wrong change by mistake, gives the child a suggestion for action, but not only that.

In listening he engages not only in judgments of fact but also in judgments of value. He not only knows but he feels and desires. He not only adds to his fund of experience concerning ways to act in a given circumstance, but he is helped to an accretion of feeling that it is good to do what appears right to one's best judgment, and to a re-enforcement of whatever value he has consciously or unconsciously put upon personal integrity.

Because of its appeal to the emotions, the story sometimes is made a tool by which the teller forces upon the child a feeling not really shared. That is, instead of constructing and telling a story which may make its own direct appeal to the hearer, the teller surcharges his material with the feeling he himself has about the facts or truths or persons involved. The sweetly sentimental stories about Jesus, for instance, found in so much children's literature, often cause an aftermath of revulsion against the counterfeit emotion they called forth, when more realistic stories might have generated soundly based and enduring appreciations.

As in the case of any art form, the story involves the interpretation of whatever section of life it portrays. A landscape artist does not reproduce the landscape before him but he paints into his picture whatever section of the scene and whatever features have significance to him for reasons which explain him as artist. The story necessarily and legitimately represents the feelings and emotions of the teller in that it represents the teller's choice of life materials in the proportion and with the emphasis he considers real and true. It is indeed a teacher's chief function to effect for his pupils some usable simplification of the great mass of mankind's experience.

The story is valuable in education because of its efficacy in providing short-cuts to experience. "One doesn't need to stand up to one's neck in experience, in a perfect muck of experience, in order to know things, in order to know that they are there. . . .

The art of getting the result, the spirit of experience itself, needs a good word spoken for it nowadays."

Actual, first-hand experiences can fail to have real experiential value. They may lack the perspective and informing power which a dramatic, interpreting story can give. It is possible for an individual to be so submerged in race hatred, for instance, that he cannot sense the meaning of race antagonisms as well as someone who has only tasted that experience through the condensed, spot-lighted insight which an interpreting great story has given. And it may be that a story "creates anew the universe after it has been annihilated in our minds by the recurrence of impressions blasted by reiteration."

It is very desirable that we give our children the spirit of many experiences which they may never have or could never have directly.

Boys and girls may have been told that the American factory in China has dealt ill with Chinese children. They will not have understood that condition in the measure possible until it was dramatized for them through the experience of a certain Zyto Bing Ling who worked in a given factory under given conditions and felt and acted in specific ways.

None of us has seen the disciples leave all and

follow Jesus. We can, however, give our pupils something of the spirit of that experience through the story. They can feel with us something of Jesus' trust in those chosen, whom he found in fishermen's boat, in custom house. Through the story boys and girls can share in a measure the response to that trust, evidenced in the ready leaving of nets, of toll booth, to follow him.

As interpretation of life, and as vicarious living, therefore, the story represents a short-cut to experience.

"The method of Science is to state, of Art to suggest." We need discussion of everyday specific situations, to be sure, but the poetic, imaginative story has a significance that should not be overlooked in the opportunity it gives to the child for his discovery of truths greater than statements of fact can convey, and of values not made articulate through analysis of his own life problems.

The child is not the harper whom the king desires to honor for his music at Christmas time, whom the king tempts with reward of gold and silver and fine horses, but who has promised "my wife and my child and my little brown dog" to be home at Christmas time, "to sing the Christmas songs at my own fireside." The child does not need to leave a sumptuous royal court to brave wind and storm and snow and forest to keep that particular promise. But his imagination is stirred by the engaging harper who kept his promise at all odds, and he will have satisfaction in discovering for himself the meaning of promises, of love and loyalty, as portrayed in this story.

In character education the indirectness of the story method commends it. Through too much unrelieved discussion of everyday personal problems, character education can endanger its ends by fostering priggishness and self-conscious goodness. The dangers of the very necessary specific application can be counterbalanced by opportunity for the child to lose himself in an atmosphere of suggested nobility in the world of story lore.

A story has value not only in the one specific direction for which it may have been given a place in the curriculum. The very fact that it represents a spread of values, that it occasions fringe thoughts and fringe apprehensions is one of its assets.

Perhaps the story of Raphael's painting of the Sistine Madonna has been chosen for telling so that children may appreciate how "one painter used his talents, his brushes and his paints to help people in their worship," but the story can also be efficacious in creating an appreciation of Italy and Italians, of the work of artists in general, of the values in great paintings. It may, however slightly, help engender the religious feeling of devotion and willingness to sacrifice which the story portrays as the meaning of the artist's message realized by those who lose themselves in the contemplation of the picture.

The story can give the hearer many intuitions which may be the basis of later more definite apprehensions.

The educator does not expect or want magic, and the story is never magic. Sometimes it is poorly chosen, or poorly developed, or very poorly told, or is only called a story and is not really one at all. But the right story, in the right place, at the right time, rightly told, uses the magic wand of interest in the direction of many great values and therefore a defense of its use does not easily claim too much.

THE TELLING OF STORIES

Sometimes a story is ineffective because it is a poor story, not worth the telling. Sometimes it is a good story in the wrong place. Often it is a good story in the right place, gone savorless because the teller is not prepared to tell it. A hurried reading, making possible only a vague general memory, has passed for preparation.

In the telling, as result, the element of suspense is lost because of omissions and unwise dilations and dilutions. Vividness is lost because colorful phrases and words just did not come to mind fast enough. Incidents that happened to impress themselves in memory are dwelt upon with unction when their effectiveness may have depended upon concise understatement. Homiletic habits and lack of respect for children's intelligence get the best of the teller and he interrupts the action of the story to elucidate meanings.

When he has finished he is more or less conscious of the fact that his story did not "go across." Then, although theoretically he hates "moralizing" and "sermonizing," and although, theoretically, he suspects his attempt is vain, still, he indulges in a frantic endeavor to push his story across by appending a little homily on the values the story was to have dramatized, and which the children would have discovered themselves to their great pleasure if these values had been left in the story for discovery.

As for interest in a story so told—such dealing with the material is like the mother's who realized, after the child's dinner, that she had forgotten to salt the soup and quickly administered afterward a pinch in a spoon to retrieve the lack. Of course, neither the dinner nor the aftermath was palatable.

For good measure of advice to tellers the author presumes to append some didactic doggerel she once concocted for a class studying story-telling:

WHAT MAKES A STORY

(GIVEN, TO BEGIN WITH, A STORY WORTH TELLING)

A sentence or two of when and where
And who it was that lived then and there,
And then the events in rising succession,—
No going afield in descriptive digression,
But telling what happened in colorful phrase,
As straight to the climax the interest you raise.
Then a conclusion, without ado,—
As always, finish when you are through.
   And *that's* what makes a story.

A teller who knows what he's going to tell,
(A story's a thing you can't bluff very well)—
Not memorized and said by rote,—
(That would give it a very mechanical note!)
But learned in a living, vital way,
By giving the words and incidents play
On your own imagination's screen,—
For only pictures vividly seen
Can be vividly painted for other's eyes,—
So know it well, or you'll blur a prize,
   For *that's* what makes a story.

Though you've told it to pillows a-squat in a row,
To the books on your shelves, who have listened just so,
Though you've told it to pictures on the wall,
(Rather tell it to them than not tell it at all,
For practice you must, so practice it well!)
The story's not finished until you tell
It at last to the children. Their spirits bright
Will kindle the story to living light,—
   It is *they* who make the story!

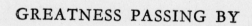
GREATNESS PASSING BY

HIS HONOR, THE JUDGE

SUPPOSE you had read in the paper one day the news: "Judge Bloman dead; State Supreme Court adjourned; County Circuit Court will attend funeral in a body." Possibly you would have thought of the one who had died as a dignified, white-haired old man, who had been in office many years. It would never have occurred to you, unless you had happened to know, that this important person could be a young boy. But this highly respected judge and citizen really was a little, undersized, red-headed, homeless boy, only thirteen years old.

Four years before this time the police had looked for him along the railroad tracks, on the outskirts of the city. Several thoughtful men and women had called at the police station to say that a very dirty, swearing, tobacco-chewing little street Arab was going about with a band of tramps, begging food for them in the town. The child should be taken from those companions, these people said, and given a chance to go to school.

The police found him and sent him to the Children's Court in the city, where the judge, a friend of boys in trouble, questioned him. The boy said his name was Frederick Bloman. He did not know where he was born nor did he remember his mother or recall that he had ever had a home. He said that one of the hoboes called him son but that the others insisted the man was not his father. He had been in many cities and towns but he did not know the names of any of them.

The good judge, who knew boys very well, noticed something about Fred that gave him hope for the boy's future. Probably he could not have told himself what it was that caused him to trust Fred to make something of his life. At any rate, the judge decided he would not send him to the reform school where the most unruly boys must go, but would give him a better opportunity to become a good citizen by making him a member of the Republic School out in the country.

This was a school where the most hopeful of the boys from the Juvenile Court were sent, a place where boys could learn to become good citizens through planning, dividing, and doing their own work, making their own laws, and managing all their own affairs.

It sounds like a nice place, doesn't it? And it was nice, but not in Fred's first estimation. As far back as his memory took him he had never slept in a bed, and he did not at all like spending his nights between sheets.

He had never eaten from a dining-table and it irked him to be expected to behave properly at meal times, and being taught manners was a great bore. He could see no sense in it. Always he had been dirty, and always he had done as he pleased. Cleanliness and courtesy had no meaning at all for him.

But Fred had a very strong sense of fair play, developed in his life among the hoboes, and he was an observing lad. So it came that he noticed how his unco-operative spirit made life less happy for other people.

He thought, "These people have only my own good in mind. It is not fair that I set myself against them." Then he began to go to bed without objecting, and to take an interest in good table manners, although for a long time he found it difficult to live up to the rules.

All the boys knew Fred Bloman before he had been at the school very long. At first they noticed him because he was so very unruly, but very soon for other reasons. Twice a week, with all the other boys in the school, Fred attended the court session. In this court, presided over by one of the boys as judge, the group made the rules that governed their life together, heard offenders tried and sentenced.

It was an acknowledged mark of good citizenship in this school republic for a boy to be willing to report any lawlessness or disobedience he had seen, or of which he had been guilty himself. Although Fred found it difficult to obey rules he told against himself when he had been disobedient, and accepted without a murmur whatever punishment the judge put upon him,—perhaps a fine of money he had earned, or the forfeit of playtime or of some other privilege.

The boys noticed that Fred took his citizenship duties seriously and they also noticed again and again, when some particularly hard problem came before the court, that it was Fred who suggested the way to solve it. "He's fair, and he's smart," they said to one another.

So it happened that when Fred was about twelve years old, and election time came for this boys' republic, the citizens nominated him for the position of judge, the highest honor in the Republic. The superintendent of the school was troubled, because Fred had begun only recently to live in an orderly way with other people.

"That is a very important position," he said, "and Fred is very young, quite too young. He is not experienced enough." He suggested that since Fred was so young they could well wait to nominate him at a later time. "There is another election six months from now, boys," he reminded. "Keep Fred in mind for then!"

But the boys elected Fred by a large majority in spite of their superintendent's warnings, and that was one of the times when boys' judgment was better than the judgment of grown-ups. For Fred became their most effective and trusted judge. People who had never before heard of the Republic School for Boys learned about it through his fame. Judges and lawyers from the city came out to visit his court sessions and hear him make judgments.

Fred was strict with the boys and they seemed to like it. One time he brought charges against a boy for quitting a ball game in which the Republic team was playing against the team of a neighboring village. The captain of the team had been unjust to this boy, who became angry and felt he had a right to quit. A substitute had to be put in who could not play as well.

The superintendent of the school thought Fred should not press the case, because, he said, "There is no law about leaving a ball game." "No," said Fred, "but there is a law about quitting." He found the boy guilty of quitting, of failing to finish a thing he had undertaken to do. "Jim was representing the Republic," said Fred, "and he had no right to think about his feelings just then."

At times Fred still found it difficult to be a good citizen. It was particularly hard not to be mischievous in school, for some of the vagabond was still in him and he could not easily sit still for any length of time.

Smoking was against the laws of the Republic. One day one of the boys persuaded an outsider to leave some tobacco in a hiding place beside the road, where the culprit found it and shared it with some of the others when they went to the creek for a swim. Fred, who had been an incessant smoker before he came to the Republic, found the temptation too much for him. He smoked with the others.

Then he realized he was a lawbreaker. So he brought complaint against himself for breaking the law that forbade smoking. As an officer of the state he was tried by the superintendent of the school, who fined him the limit. Then Fred brought suit against the others who had smoked and made the same judgment against all except the one who smuggled the tobacco in, whom he gave a double punishment.

None of the boys whom he sentenced were angry with Fred. "He was fair," they said.

When Fred had almost completed two six months terms as judge he became very ill. It did not enter the boys' minds to choose anyone else, and he was nominated for a third term while he was sick in the hospital. They were asked, "What about the judge's work if Fred should be sick a while?" "We'll take care of that problem," they said, and created the office of associate judge, to provide for the court during Fred's illness. Although Fred was desperately ill as the time for voting came, he was re-elected, but before the election day was over Fred had died.

Then the boys of the Republic learned that Fred was highly respected not only among them. A "genius from the gutters," the newspapers called him, and told of his roaming, homeless, motherless childhood, and how he had become the head of the Republic, to be noted for his tact, his fairmindedness, his originality. Surprised at the discovery, the boys said, "Things done in our school make a difference to many people outside!" and they realized that no one has any excuse for not amounting to something.

The judges and lawyers of the city held a memorial meeting for Fred. A State Supreme Court justice travelled a hundred miles to come to the funeral and the Probate Court of the county adjourned in his honor.

The funeral services were held in the cathedral in the city, with many distinguished people as mourners. During that time the boys in the Republic School held their own memorial services. No grown-up was present; it was all according to the boys' own planning. One boy after another rose to tell the story of some kindness Fred had done him personally, or of something Fred had done for the good of them all. One of the boys led in a prayer he had thought out himself, and then they all said the Lord's prayer together. It was a very beautiful service.

That was years ago, but the boys who are at the Republic School now know well the story of Fred Bloman and they regard him as their special hero. By the pool where they go swimming in summer there

8

is a drinking-fountain designed by one of the city's well-known artists. In the centre is an inscription which reads: "Frederick Bloman, Judge from March 1910 till he died, September 7, 1911." In a circle around this are the words, "I would be true for there are those who trust me."

CONSEQUENCES

THE clang of the twenty-minutes-till-supper gong caused a merry scramble in the creek on Mrs. Green's farm, where the boys from the reform school over the hill were having their daily dip. Everyone wanted one more swim, wanted once more to "duck" some other boy. Presently the splashing was over, clothes were quickly found, and the boys were running up the hill, smoothing wet hair, buttoning overall straps.

Two of the boys, big Tom and little Larry, for some reason did not feel like hurrying. As they were lagging behind the rest, taking time to look about, Tom's attention was caught by a proud gander in Mrs. Green's barnyard, stalking about among his flock of geese with the air of one owning the world. "He's too proud," thought Tom. "I'll fix him." So he picked up a stone, threw it, and very narrowly missed hitting his majesty the gander, who promptly began to hiss and sputter and to flap his wings in hurt dignity, even though nothing else about him was hurt.

Little Larry laughed loudly at the gander's funny look of injured pride. "Watch me!" called Tom, encouraged by Larry's enjoyment, and ran through the open door of the chicken house. Larry suspected what would happen, and thought, "Teasing her fowls and robbing her chicken house isn't a nice way to pay Mrs. Green for letting us swim in her creek!" He was about to call to Tom, "Don't do that!" but already Tom appeared, his hands full of eggs.

"What next!" wondered Larry, fascinated by the actions of the excited gander and the possibilities of Tom's next move. The gander came toward Tom, head down, flapping his wings. Larry laughed loudly. Tom quickly handed Larry an egg, they both took aim, and one egg, either Larry's or Tom's, hit the gander right in the middle of the back, spattering his white grandeur with the yellow of the yolk.

How the gander sputtered, and what quacking and squawking and cackling there was in the excited barnyard! Someone appeared on the porch of the farmhouse and the boys took to their heels with amazing speed. Perhaps their hurry was partly in fear of the gander, although they would not have acknowledged that a gander could really frighten them.

All out of breath they arrived in the dining-room

11

of the school, just barely in time for supper. Larry did not eat with as much relish as he usually did. He was a thoughtful boy and his conscience hurt him. He was thinking so hard that he was forgetting to chew.

It was a rule of the school, he remembered, and considered a mark of good citizenship, to report any wrong one had done. "I'll report," Larry said to himself, "and take my medicine, and it won't make any difference except to me. One egg thrown away couldn't really make any difference on a farm where there are so many dozen. And the gander's nerves will be calm by now."

After supper he found Tom and suggested they make a joint report, but Tom said, "Not me! We didn't do anything worth making a fuss over! No reason why anybody should know about it!" Larry announced, "I'll tell on myself, then!" "Go ahead," said Tom.

"Maybe I won't after all," thought Larry. There would be a fine to pay and perhaps work assigned for play time. But he was an honest lad, and anxious to keep up his record as a good citizen. "I'll do it. I'll keep the rules and report," he decided. "The punishment will be over quickly," he consoled him-

12

self, "and then the whole thing will be forgotten."

So he found a slip of paper and wrote on it, "Threw egg in Mrs. Green's barnyard. Made the gander mad." In a spirit of bravado he added, "Will take the consequences," then signed it "Larry Brown." He found the complaint box, stuck the paper into it, and with a feeling of relief saw it disappear down the slot.

The next was a day of sizzling heat and the boys looked forward to swimming-time with special eagerness. They were to have their own swimming-pool, but until it was built they could have only one swim a day, for the superintendent did not want them to invade the kind neighbor's farm more often. To-day they had to wait for their swim until after the weekly court session.

Suddenly excited word went around, "No swimming to-day!" "No swimming?" "Why not?" "Who says so?" "A notice on the bulletin board says so!" Sure enough! "No swimming this afternoon" said a notice, and that was all it said. Consternation and bewilderment reigned among the boys. What was it all about? What could be the reason? The superintendent of the school wore a serious, disturbed expression.

13

CONSEQUENCES

Time came for the court session and all the boys filed into the court-room. Since this was a self-governing school the boys had a court in which to make and administer their own laws. The boy who had been elected judge sat at the table in front, with the secretary of the court beside him, who began to read the charges against the various offenders of the week.

One group of boys did not keep their table clean, —that was a complaint from the boy in charge of the dining-room. The judge imposed a fine on each of the group to help them remember not to spill their food. Several boys detailed to mow the lawn had not returned the lawn mowers to their places. Two boys had overstayed their time at tennis. So the charges went on.

Presently Larry heard his name called. Trembling with excitement he rose to his feet, to hear the reading of the complaint he had written against himself. "I am only nervous," he said to himself, "not afraid," for he felt sure the judge would not take his case very seriously.

The secretary read what Larry had written, "Threw egg in Mrs. Green's barnyard. Made the gander mad." Larry was surprised to see that the judge seemed not the least bit amused. The secretary

14

read on, "Will take the consequences. Larry Brown." Nobody seemed to see anything funny about that either.

The judge looked very serious as he said, "Hold that charge. There is another one that has to do with the same thing, against both Larry and Tom. Tom Clark, you rise too."

As the two boys, Tom and Larry, stood before him, the secretary read a complaint against them signed by the officers of the Republic. It charged Tom and Larry with taking from all the boys the right to swim in Mrs. Green's creek. There was a murmur of disapproval through the court-room which sounded to Larry's guilty ears like a great rumble.

"Mrs. Green was very nice," said the judge, "to let us come to her farm every day. She says that there has been trouble with the boys of this school at different times which she has been willing to overlook, but that going into her hen house and stealing eggs to tease her chickens and other fowls was the last straw. She feels she cannot have us there any more. Tom and Larry are said to be guilty, and Larry confesses. Are there any witnesses?"

Several boys testified they had seen Larry and

15

Tom lagging behind and had heard furious squawking and quacking shortly afterward. "Guilty?" asked the judge of Larry. "Guilty, your honor," Larry confessed. "Tom Clark, are you guilty?" asked the judge. "Guilty. your honor," confessed shamefaced Tom.

"There have been many complaints against Tom," said the judge. "He does not seem to know how to act in a school of citizens, who govern themselves. I'll send him back to the judge of the Juvenile Court in the city." Tom hung his head. He knew the judge in the City Court might not give him another chance. He, too, might think Tom was not promising enough as a future citizen to stay in the school where he now was, and would send him to the kind of reform school that was more like a prison, where there was no freedom to misuse.

Larry felt very sad about his friend's plight. There was much good in Tom, even if he was often naughty and thoughtless. "He's always been good to me," thought Larry, "looked after me because he thought I was homesick."

The judge addressed Larry. "You are young, Larry, you haven't been here long. You can't be expected to know so well what is expected of you. It's a sure thing Tom put you up to it. And you did report on yourself. Of course, it's silly of you to say you'll take the consequences. You must see you can't."

Larry was beginning to see that. The judge went on: "All of us have to take the consequences. There'll be baths in bath tubs only after this, for all of us, and that's no particular fun. I'll fine you three dollars from your earnings. That's enough extra punishment, since you can't go swimming either any more."

"It was my fault too," spoke up Larry. "Next case, please," the judge directed the secretary. Larry had to sit down.

He did not know what happened during the remainder of the court session—his thoughts kept him so busy. A guilty conscience told him that, had he not laughed approvingly and thereby encouraged thoughtless Tom, all this trouble might not have come. At other times Tom, though naughty, had not been stubborn. From the start Tom had seemed to like him and had shown himself easily subject to his influence. "Probably Tom would have listened to me," Larry decided.

He had learned it was a rule of the school that any

judgment of the court would be reconsidered if five boys signed a request to that effect. "Don't worry yet," he whispered to Tom, who sat just in front of him. "I'll try to get the fellows to have the court reconsider your case. It was my fault too."

Then Larry sat back to listen to the court proceedings and to take his citizen's part in giving thought to them. But his mind wandered back to his own problem.

"The judge is right, I can't take the consequences," he said to himself. "Tom is taking them, for he may have to leave this school. Mrs. Green doesn't feel friendly to this school and trust the boys as she used to. The gander,—well, he's probably got over being mad. But the boys, they all have to pay,—none of them can go swimming any more."

It did not seem like justice to Larry that so many people should have to pay consequences. But somehow it appeared that was the way in life.

The signal for the closing of the court session was given. The judge pounded the desk with his gavel and announced, "Court adjourned." All the boys rose to file out. Larry's eyes wandered to the motto over the judge's desk, the school motto, "All for one and one for all."

CONSEQUENCES

It startled him with new meaning. "I used to think," he said to himself, "it meant that the good we do helps others. It seems to mean, too, that the bad we do hurts other people."

THE OTHER PROPHET

AHAB was a king of the olden times, who always wanted very much whatever it was that he wanted, after the manner of the kings of the olden times. On this occasion he wanted to go to war. "It is time I went to war again," he was saying to himself very determinedly, "to war on the King of Aram. I want to go to war against Aram and that right soon. It would be well," he added thoughtfully, "to have an ally. I wonder if Jehosaphat would help me."

Just then it happened that Jehosaphat, his neighbor, the King of Judah, arrived for a visit. Ahab received his guest royally, and as soon as he thought it could be done at all politely he cut short the reception ceremonies to talk business. "Will you join me in making war on the King of Aram?" he asked. "If I go to battle against him, will you go with me?"

"Yes," said the King of Judah promptly, "I will go with you. My soldiers and horses and chariots are all ready for war, and just waiting to be useful. I will go with you; my men shall be as your men, and my horses as your horses."

He thought a minute. Jehosaphat liked too to do as he pleased, but while he did that he liked also to do what was right. So he added, "Had we not better find out first if God will be with us should we go to war? Pray, find out what God has to say!"

The King of Israel was not particularly interested in learning God's will, for he wanted to follow his own inclinations. However, he was anxious to be a gracious host to his royal guest, so he sent out a messenger with the command, "Send for my court prophets, all of them. Tell them I must inquire of them the will of God."

They were called prophets, these men who professed to know the will of God, but most of them were merely soothsayers and some of them were fakirs. The King of Israel paid their salaries and they were anxious to please him. At the king's command they came, 400 of them, all knowing that he had been preparing for war, that he had been getting chariots and men and provisions ready for the march.

All their eyes were searchingly upon the king, as he asked them, "Shall I carry out my plan of battle and march against the King of Aram or shall I give it up?"

21

They answered quickly and with one accord, "March against him, go to battle. The Lord will deliver him into the hands of the king."

One of these so-called prophets, who wanted to make a special impression on his king, came rushing in with some iron horns tied to his head, and cried out, "As a bull uses his horns to rout his enemies, so you will push the Arameans until they perish."

The other prophets, excited by the prospect of war and of the king's favor, danced about the throne, clapped their hands and chanted, "March, march, go to battle, the Lord will be with you."

The visiting king, the King of Judah, was very silent as he listened. He was not at all convinced. It seemed strange to him that all the prophets were so enthusiastic, and so sure that the thing the king wanted to do was what God wanted.

He asked, "Is there not a prophet somewhere besides these, a prophet of God, whom we might consult, to learn God's will?" "Someone," he probably felt like adding, "who sounds more sincere than these servile fellows do."

"Ye-e-es," the King of Israel answered with some hesitation, though he immediately had someone in mind. "There is one other, Micaiah, the son of Im-

22

lah, but I do not like him because he does not like me. He never prophesies good concerning me but only evil."

The King of Judah answered politely, "Let not the king say so!" which meant to say, "How could he have anything against you!"

Ahab knew very well that Micaiah did have very many reasons for being critical of him. However, since the royal guest was really expecting to hear what that prophet might have to say, Ahab called an officer and bade him, "Go quickly, and bring before us Micaiah, the prophet."

The officer found Micaiah and explained why he was wanted. As they were walking along together he put his hand on Micaiah's shoulder and said, "Let me give you some good advice. All the other prophets told the king good news. Let your message be as theirs. Give the king good news also. Tell him what he would like to hear." But Micaiah answered, "As God lives, whatsoever God tells me to say, that will I say."

As Micaiah came near he saw the two kings, arrayed in royal robes, seated grandly on two thrones, surrounded by the army of prophets, but he was not dismayed. The prophets were talking loudly to each other, that their king might hear their words. Micaiah heard them say, "Our king will march against the enemy and win. The Lord will put the enemy into the hands of the king."

Suddenly they stood quiet for they were watching Micaiah as he was led forward. The king of Israel asked, "Micaiah, shall we carry out our plan and march to attack the King of Aram or shall we give it up?"

Micaiah, who had prayed about the impending war, answered, "You would not win the battle. I saw all Israel scattered upon the mountains like sheep that have no shepherd."

He saw the king frown darkly and glance at his guest as if to say, "I told you so," but Micaiah finished what he had to say. "The Lord said to me," he went on, "let every man return to his home in peace."

The King of Israel turned to the King of Judah and snapped out, "Did I not tell you he would not prophesy any good for me but only evil?" To the officer he gave command, "Take Micaiah to be clapped into prison. Have him fed on bread and water to keep him miserable till I come home victorious."

24

Micaiah felt sorry for the king. Warning him again he said quietly, "If ever you return home victorious, then the Lord has not spoken through me."

The officer marched Micaiah off to prison. "It is too bad," he said, as they were on the way, "that you did not tell the king what he wanted to hear. You would be free now." "Free?" asked Micaiah, "I would not call it freedom to be afraid to tell the truth that God has spoken to me!"

Into the prison went Micaiah, but he went with a resolute heart and with a mind at peace. The king went to war and to his doom. In a great slaughter he was killed and his army routed.

A ZINC-LINED PIANO

WHEN Albert Schweitzer was just a little boy in his home in Alsace, before ever he went to school, he was able to remember any melody he had heard and to play it by ear in such a manner that everyone admired him for it.

His family understood about Albert's gift for music, and while his parents saw to it that he had some instruction and help at the piano, they let him enjoy his talent fairly much as he pleased.

When he was only about ten years old, Albert had to leave home to go to a higher school—the kind of adventure most of us do not set out upon until we go to college. He was sent to the home of an uncle and aunt some distance away in order that he might attend the school in their town.

They were very good to him and he loved them dearly but they kept him under stricter discipline than was the rule in his own home. The thing that irked him particularly was his aunt's insistence upon regular piano practice. He could have such a good time at the piano without so much hard work at all those exercises—so why, he asked, should he practise when he would like to read stories, when he could frolic with his friends, or when he might be playing the piano just for fun, as his fancy dictated? But his aunt was not easily cajoled.

At noon, after his luncheon, Albert had to practise until it was time to return to school, and in the afternoon, when his home work was finished, he had to go to the piano again. When he objected his aunt would say to him, "You don't know what your music may mean to you when you are grown." Being grown seemed a long time off to Albert, and he preferred enjoying himself now.

But he practised because he must, and then, almost without realizing it, the time came when he took pleasure in practice. He did not have to wait to grow up to have his music mean much to him, for he was able to play more and more beautiful compositions, and to express his thoughts and feelings ever better through his fingers on the keys. He had the ambition to play a great organ, as his father and grandfather were able to do, and when he was fifteen the organist in a great church in the city let him practise on his organ, a wonderful instrument, with three keyboards and sixty-two stops.

By the time he was sixteen he was permitted to

take this organist's place in the regular church services, and later in that year he accompanied the choir of the church in a great concert directed by his friend, the organist. His joy was so great in being able to send forth such beautiful harmonies in the pleasing tones of the wonderful organ that he no longer begrudged any amount of practice.

There was a time in his later life when he was probably still more happy over the work he had put into the development of his talent. He had come to be a famous writer and teacher in the University of Strassburg, but the needs of the people in Africa gave his mind no peace. "In Europe," he said to himself, "there is no kind of illness for which people cannot get some help from the doctors. If cure is not possible, at least pain can be made more easy to bear. In Africa there are thousands and thousands of people who have no doctors or hospitals, no way of benefiting from all that doctors and nurses have learned—hundreds and thousands of people are dying in their pain without any help!"

Albert Schweitzer decided, "These needy people are my own responsibility. I must not depend upon others to help them. I must go myself to do what I can." So he studied to become a physician, while his wife learned to be a nurse. Professor Schweitzer became Doctor Schweitzer, but that was not all he did to get ready.

Some friends gave money for his enterprise, but the hospital he wanted to build, the drugs and medicines and instruments he would need, the cost of the trip, and many other expenses, meant that he needed more money than he had at his disposal. Thanks to his music there was a way out of the difficulty.

Although music was not his profession he had a reputation far and wide as organist. Albert Schweitzer was known to be the best of interpreters of the music of the great composer Bach. So in Germany, in France, and in England he gave organ concerts, interpreting the music of Bach. The proceeds of these concerts, with the income from a book on Bach he had written, made possible his mission to Africa, earned him enough money that he could set out to do the thing he so much wanted to do.

He remembered his aunt as she said, "You don't know what your music may mean to you when you are grown," and smiled. "She could not have dreamed," he said, "that one day my music would help me collect the funds for starting a hospital in the primeval forest."

A ZINC–LINED PIANO

With the help of his music money Doctor Schweitzer built his hospital and helped throngs of people who were suffering from the terrible diseases of the tropics. From miles and miles about the natives came bringing sick friends and relatives to the Christian doctor. One day an old man and his wife, suffering from leprosy, arrived at the hospital hardly able to stand, they were so exhausted. They had rowed themselves 250 miles upstream to get to the doctor.

Perhaps he would have broken under the strain of the very hard work, the sight of so much suffering, the many anxieties, the loneliness for friends and home, if it had not been for a certain recreation and pleasure that was made possible for him.

One day he heard the whistle of the steamer that came at intervals up the river through the jungle, and the sound made him very happy. He knew that on board were packing-cases full of medicines for the hospital and also a very special, very heavy case.

A society in Paris for whom Doctor Schweitzer had been organist had caused a special piano to be built for him, to show him their gratitude for his services to them. They knew that an ordinary piano would not last very long in the tropics, therefore

30

they had provided one made with a zinc-lined case to protect the instrument from the termites and other tropical insects and from the great dampness.

The new home in the tropics had not seemed like home without an instrument to play, and we can imagine how eagerly Doctor Schweitzer awaited the coming of the promised piano. But he was troubled, for the steamer on which it had come up the big river could not navigate the branch stream on which the doctor lived. Surely no canoe could carry so heavy a burden, he thought.

He learned that there was one which could. One of the storekeepers at the port owned a canoe hollowed out of a tree so gigantic that it could have carried five pianos, and in that huge canoe the doctor's piano travelled the last part of its journey.

A number of natives rowed the canoe upstream. When it arrived at the mission station a large group, including even the school children, was ready and eager to help carry the cargo. Doctor Schweitzer wrote his friends how the piano case and each of the other boxes "suddenly got a crowd of black legs under it and two rows of woolly heads apparently growing out of its sides," and how, "amid shouting and shrieking, it thus crept up the hill!"

After that the piano in his bungalow was a refuge where the doctor lost himself in music for a little while every day in the noon recess, and often in the evening. Sometimes he was so weary in body and soul from all the suffering he had seen and the work he had done to relieve it, that he wondered how he could face another day. Then he would go to his piano and under his fingers the masters of music of the ages would bring him beauty for pain and strength for weariness.

He came to deeper and deeper enjoyment and appreciation of the music he had studied before, and he had pleasure and recreation from his playing which would not have been possible if he had been less a master at it.

Again he had reason to remember his aunt as she said, "You don't know what your music may mean to you when you are grown."

MICHAEL'S ACQUAINTANCES

MANY of the telephone appliances we use every day, and numerous other electrical things that have come to seem very necessary in our lives, are the inventions of the great scientist, Professor Michael Pupin. Besides being a great scientist and inventor, Professor Pupin is a leader among those who help people see the presence of God in the wonders of nature and of science.

When Michael Pupin, a Serbian shepherd lad, landed at Ellis Island, the immigration officials shook their heads over him. The officials thought they had ample reason to shake their heads over him, for how could they let loose in a strange country a boy who had only five cents in his pocket!

And what good was a carfare to him who had no place to go? For he had confessed that he had no relatives in America and knew no one. On second thought Michael informed them that he did have some acquaintances. He knew Lincoln, he said, and Franklin, and Harriet Beecher Stowe, whose book, "Uncle Tom's Cabin" he had read in translation.

"You showed good taste," acknowledged the officials, "in your choice of American acquaintances." But they shook their heads again and did not know what to do with the lad. What good, possibly, could those acquaintances do, who had all died long ago!

When the officials asked him about his history, he told with great feeling about his forebears among the liberty-loving guardians of the Austrian frontier, their struggles for freedom and right. He told of Prince Marko, who, he said, was the Abraham Lincoln of Serbia, a defender of the oppressed, and of Saint Sava, his mother's hero, who had done so much for the education of the boys and girls of Serbia.

He himself had come to America, Michael said, because it was a country of political freedom and because there had lived in it a man like the inventor Benjamin Franklin, who had discovered things about light and sound.

The officials saw how bright the lad was, and ambitious, and self-reliant. They did not like to disappoint him—he was so eager. They discussed him with each other a while, and then agreed to let him stay, directing him to the Labor Bureau, where American citizens came to hire immigrants to work for them.

While he was waiting there one of the officials came to talk with him. "We made an exception in your case," he told Michael. "You must look sharp and get a job quickly."

Michael did not understand. Why did he have to be an exception? While he sat waiting for his job he did much thinking.

"I am bringing much to America," he thought. "I am rich."

His father and mother, and the people of his home village as they gathered winter evenings around the fireside in his home, telling stories and singing ballads of their people's history, had taught him that he was rich. He was rich in the memories of the glorious history of his race, in the stories of heroes he knew so well that they were a part of him. He had been brought up to consider these memories very proud possessions and he would try to live up to them. Would not that make him a good citizen? And the stories of the great Americans he revered— were they not wealth too? (He could study light and sound as Benjamin Franklin had done, and he could help the oppressed, after Abraham Lincoln!)

As the lad thought of the great characters whose influence upon him he was bringing with him to

35

America, his parents stood out among them, his father tall and dark, with the shining eyes he could never forget. He had been one of the leaders of the liberty-loving men of the native village. And his mother with the saintly light in her eyes! He came to think that neither Raphael nor Titian had ever painted a more beautiful saint than was the mother who had taught him to see God in his universe and to live in his presence, the mother who would not let him come home on the death of the father to take over the burdens of the head of the house, but insisted that he must pursue his education.

"Knowledge," he remembered she had said to him, "is the golden ladder over which we climb to heaven, knowledge is the light which illuminates our path through this life and leads to a future life of everlasting glory."

"I am rich," he said to himself. "No matter what the officials think."

A Delaware farmer came to the Labor Bureau where Michael sat waiting. Looking for a strong boy to be a farm helper, he hired Michael and the two set off together.

Michael had not much baggage to carry. Since he had had no money to buy his passage to America he

36

had sold his yellow sheepskin coat, and the black sheepskin cap his mother had given him, also his watch and his books, and the sale had brought him just enough money to buy his steamship ticket to America. The only possessions he had when he began his work on the farm were the clothes on his back, a few changes of linen, and a red fez, which he wore as a hat because no one had been willing to buy it.

Presently he guided a plow on a Delaware farm, wearing the red Turkish fez until he could afford to buy a hat.

He learned English and found his bearings in the new country and earned his living and saved money for an education. When employers suggested that he was doing rather well without further education he told the story of the ambitions of Saint Sava for Serbian boys and girls and quoted his mother saying, "Knowledge is the golden ladder over which we climb to heaven."

He went to college and worked and planned and thought and experimented, and finally became the great scientist he is.

When one day he was sailing from America to Europe to visit his old home, Michael Pupin remembered the day when he had first landed in America, when he had sat at the Labor Bureau with only five cents in his pocket. He recalled how the great of Serbia had passed by in his memory and he thought of the great characters in American history he had learned to know.

He said, "The best thing I brought when I came to America was the inspiration of the great of my country, the best thing I am taking back home with me from America is the inspiration of the greatness that is in American history and life.

A SURPRISE PACKAGE

WHEN John Rodgers was a boy his mother celebrated special days by surprising him with little gifts. The first day of school, his birthday, or the day he was leaving on a vacation, would become very special days, for in a package beside his breakfast plate John would find something he much needed or wanted. There would be a new necktie or shirt, some roller skates, or perhaps an interesting book to read. John and his mother both found so much joy in the practice that she continued it long after John was grown.

When John became a man he joined the navy. He sailed the wide world in Uncle Sam's big ships, and whenever he left his home port for a long journey his mother slipped something into his bag to surprise and please him when he would come upon it in unpacking.

John was a very bright and dependable young man and he was promoted again and again. The navy began to build airplanes and some of the navy's sailors became fliers. One of these was John.

The big airplanes made longer and longer journeys. At last the President of the United States said, "Let us see whether an airplane can fly from San Francisco to Hawaii!" That is a long journey—several thousand miles long, and it must be made without stopping.

The men in the government looked about for the best man to command such a flight and they chose John. He was Commander John now, and they said to him, "See if you can fly from San Francisco to Hawaii, away in the middle of the Pacific Ocean."

John wrote his mother to tell her all about the plan. She was very proud but also very worried. Would John be able to make the trip without falling into the ocean? And if he fell into the ocean, would he be rescued? Suppose the big flying-ship landed in the ocean, what would John and his men have to eat and drink until ships might find them? So she anxiously reflected as she tried to decide what kind of a present to give her son.

It must not take up much room, she realized, for there is not much space on airplanes, and it must be something that would be of particular help if John and his crew should have trouble.

Then she thought of something that seemed just right. She sent it to her son and wrote: "Dear John:

40

If you should get into trouble on the ocean you will need what is in this little package. Do not open it until you need it."

John read his mother's letter and laughed to himself. "Mothers always think of trouble," he said, "but they save a boy much trouble by thinking of it ahead of time. I wonder what it is Mother got for me!" He put the little package into a safe place and soon everything was ready for the journey.

High up in the air they sailed over the ocean. Hour after hour the motors throbbed away, mile after mile of gray sea slipped behind. Now the end of the journey was near. A few hours more, not many hundred miles beyond, and Hawaii would appear, the great flight would be over, and all the world would rejoice.

Then a great west wind arose. Straight into the teeth of the wind the fliers fought their way but the plane flew slower now and the gasoline supply began to fail. Then it was gone—and the great plane glided down on the desert of sea.

Though the radio was without power and no word could be sent anywhere, John and his four companions expected it would be only a short time before a nearby ship would pick them up. But no ship came. Days passed and still there was no ship. Sometimes a smudge of smoke on the horizon gave them hope, only to make them doubt it had been smoke at all.

"Surely they are searching for us," the men said to each other. They knew they had drifted very far from their course and their voices did not sound quite as hopeful as their words.

The men became very hungry and still more thirsty. As you must know, on the ocean, because of the saltiness, the old word is true, "Water, water, everywhere, nor any drop to drink."

The men were wondering how they could survive much longer without water to drink. They were thinking of their loved ones, how they would be sorrowing if they knew of all the present danger. "Will we ever see them again?" the fliers asked themselves.

Then Commander John remembered his mother's gift. He pulled it from its hiding-place and showed the package to the men. "My mother said not to open it," he explained, "unless we should get into trouble." "We're in trouble now, for sure," agreed the men. Eagerly Commander John opened the little package, the men crowding about to see what might be in it.

42

What should they see but a little machine called a still, which takes the salt out of water and so makes ocean water fit to drink! With cries of joy the men put the machine to work and soon they all had a drink of clean water.

Day followed day; the men were hungry but at least they were not thirsty, and hunger is not as hard to bear as thirst. On the ninth day, when all the world had decided, "Commander John and his crew are drowned!" a ship was sighted, and never did a ship look more friendly to any group. They were found by the searching ship, picked up, and taken into the harbor some few hundred miles away. Radio messages were sent to the other searching ships. Cable and radio told anxious people all over the world, "Commander John and his crew have been found."

When they came into port at Honolulu thousands of people welcomed them and rejoiced that they were living. The people asked, "How did you stay alive without anything to eat or drink?" Commander John Rodgers showed them the little machine and explained the way it worked. He looked very proud and happy as he said, "We owe our lives to my mother's thoughtfulness."

43

THE TERMITES

IN the tropical countries there lives a little creature which is commonly known by its nickname, the "white ant." But this interesting little creature is not white at all, and it is not even related to the ant, who is its worst enemy. Better than its nickname, therefore, is its real name, the "termite."

Many people never learn how interesting the termite is. "Who wants to know about the termite," they say, "the naughty little insect that comes with whole armies of his relatives, with millions of them, to eat up people's houses and furniture and trees!"

But, of course, you can't expect the little termite to understand what a human being's home means to him, nor to know the difference between a door post and some discarded piece of timber, or to see why people might wish he would eat the packing-box rather than the piano.

Anything wooden is just wood to him; all he knows about wood is that it makes food for the babies and the other members of his household, and that out of it he can make a cement house to shelter them.

It is a wonderful home that he builds, and he keeps house in it in a wonderful way. In the building of that home and in the housekeeping for the community within it each one of the millions of termites does his share.

The termites in any one colony do not look alike. Their different tasks call for different kinds of bodies. The soldier termite has not the kind of body in which cement can be made of the food of wood, and the worker termite does not carry the huge shield which is part of the soldier termite's equipment. The queen, who lays the eggs from which all the members of the colony are hatched, is different from them both, very much larger in size.

The workers have the duty, first of all, of building the great home. They begin underground, making halls and rooms and corridors, building from within outward. The house grows bigger and taller, till it commonly rises twelve feet above the ground and often twice as high as that. Since the termite is smaller than our ordinary bee, it is evident that his house is higher for him than our tall skyscrapers are for us.

But he cannot go to the top of his skyscraper to overlook the landscape and all the other skyscrapers, as human beings can do. His houses have no windows in them, not any at all, and the walls are a solid mass.

The builders use the best of materials for their walls. The cement manufactured in the worker termite's own body he squeezes out drop by drop as it is needed. When it hardens it makes walls so strong that no enemy can penetrate them, unless it be man, and man has had to use dynamite to make way for railway tracks and highways that led through a termite home.

The home is not built in any hit-or-miss fashion, here a room and there a hall, but the termite engineers and architects work according to very careful plans. No one studying the termites ever discovered draughtsmen and blue-print makers, but one might almost believe they were there, so carefully are the plans made. In order that all the members of the enormous family may go about their affairs without disorder, the termite engineers provide for a clever system of passages and corridors, leading to the tallest top, and to the basement and sub-basement underground.

46

They plan for a central heating system too, for the termites knew how to make possible through fermentation a moist, even, regulated heat before man ever thought of such a thing as central heating. There are gardens within the walls to furnish food for times of need, and storerooms in which to keep piles of chewed-up wood and cut bits of grass for future use. Low, in the centre, is built a special room for the queen. Always there is a nursery, kept warmer than the rest of the building, where the larvæ, the baby termites, no bigger than pinheads, are fed and nursed.

Even after the home seems to be finished some worker termites are always kept busy as builders. They enlarge the house as that seems necessary and they look after the repairs, so that the great home is always in the best condition.

The worker termites who are not needed as builders are busy at many household tasks. Some are gardeners, some storeroom keepers, some nursemaids to the baby termites, watching them hatch, seeing that they are kept warm, carrying food to them. A number are constantly busy as ladies-in-waiting and nurses to the queen, keeping her company, feeding her, and carrying the eggs she lays to the nursery to be hatched. 47

Always a great many of the workers are needed to bring in food. The workers have great jaws, which cross like scissors, jaws so strong that they easily cut through the toughest grass and through trees and lumber. They go out in great, well-organized armies, marching side by side in large processions. On both sides soldier termites guard the workers against their enemies, the ants, and against other creatures of the tropics who might disturb or destroy them.

The soldier termite carries a horny shield and pincers hard as steel. The burden of this armor and of the weapons is so great that it takes all the soldier's energy to carry it, and he is not provided with strong jaws like the worker. Therefore he cannot secure and prepare his own food but is dependent upon the workers to feed him. When a soldier is hungry he gently taps a worker with his feelers and the worker forthwith gives up his supply of food.

Many of the soldiers are kept busy guarding the lines of workers on their food-getting expeditions, but some of them have other duties. They guard night and day the room of the queen and some seem to act as traffic cops in places where many termites must pass to and fro in the home. They all seem to be willing to work for the good of all at whichever task is theirs.

The soldiers and the workers are all blind and without wings. The king and queen come from the only group in the nest that can see and fly. Once a year—no one knows how the signal is given—the walls at the ends of the corridors are opened by the workers for the winged ones, and then a great flight begins, somewhat like the swarming of the bees but on a much greater scale. When the flight is over possibly a few return to the nest, but all the rest of the cloud of winged ones fall dead to the ground. Perhaps they are an offering for the good of the whole —as yet no one knows much about the meaning of this flight.

When it is over, the soldiers who have guarded the openings give way to the workers, who quickly cement a new closing. The enemy ant, who likes to take the nice safe termite house for his own use, may come to invade at any moment, and so the termites work with feverish haste to close their walls tightly.

They do not come to their work pell mell, as one might expect, but in perfect order, each worker placing his little drop of cement in just the right place and marching away to make room for the succeeding one. They are so exact about their work and so orderly that one thinks there must be a foreman just around the corner directing them. In unbelievably short time the termite's nest has a solid, perfectly closed surface again, with a wall no enemy, except it be man, knows how to open.

When it happens, as it sometimes does, that the enemy ants take advantage of a crack in the wall, or of some corridor opening not yet closed, the guarding soldiers quickly sound an alarm. They beat upon the wall with their hard jaws and in a trice more soldiers appear, while the workers retreat to make room for them. With their horny shields the soldiers try to form a solid wall across the opening and so shut out the enemy. If they are hard pressed by the invaders they become very excited and send forth a high vibrating tone, which the inhabitants within answer by a whistling sound that seems to mean, "All right, coming!"

If the enemy is routed the soldiers stay on guard at the opening a while longer; then the workers come to seal the place.

It happens sometimes that the enemy gets the best of the termite soldiers. Defeat seems sure. Still they

know a way, and their co-operation in defeat is wonderful to see: When the soldiers know that they cannot oust the enemy, only enough of them stay to
keep him engaged for a time and all the rest retreat.

During the time the enemy is busy overcoming
the defending soldiers, the workers seal up the corridor very quickly a little farther back. Then the
home is out of danger, the community is again safe
behind the new walls, although a number of the
group have offered their lives to make that safety
possible.

In time of danger as in the everyday affairs of the
community, "Each for all" has seemed to be the
motto.

WHAT A JINGLE STARTED

WHEN Jean Henri Fabre was a little boy he lived with his grandparents. Their home was on a high meadow in a rocky section of country along the coast of France. The family made a living by raising sheep and cattle. Jean Henri was much interested in the cattle and the sheep, particularly the little lambs, but he cared even more about creatures of the field that were still smaller.

One day, when he was about six years old, he made a discovery which sharpened his curiosity so much that he never stopped searching for more new facts to know. He was walking along the edge of the woods in the silence of the evening when he heard a sort of jingle, coming faint and soft out of the green of the forest.

"Who is making that noise?" he asked himself. "Could it be a little bird chirping in its nest? It sounds different, somehow. I must look into that." He remembered being warned that a wolf had been seen in the woods, the wolf who had been the hero of so many of his grandmother's bed-time tales.

"I won't go too far," he assured himself, "but just

a very little nearer." Jean Henri went as near as he dared, then stood quietly to listen, but though he stayed a long time he could not learn who the singer was. At the faintest sound in the bushes the jingles would cease. He came again the next evening and the next. At last he discovered the singer: it was a special kind of little grasshopper!

Jean Henri was much excited to know about a grasshopper that sings. He would never have guessed it could be a grasshopper! And it had been such fun to discover this all by himself! The discovery had been so near home and was so interesting. Surely there must be much more to learn in the woods and meadows roundabout! But his seventh birthday came and he was sent to school, away from the woods.

Of all his class Jean Henri was the first to learn to read, and the reason was this: In his reading book there was the picture of a pigeon, with a round eye and red feet, and there was some printing beside it. Just then his father bought him a book full of animal pictures and they too had printing beside them. He knew that the printing would tell him things he wanted to know about the pigeon and about all the animals in the book, and he was so eager to learn what the words had to say that he worked and worked over his letters until the books could tell him what he wanted to know.

Even the best nature books printed when Jean Henri was a boy did not tell so very much. Some little creatures were not mentioned at all and about others there was not more to be found than their names, because no one had studied them sufficiently to know enough to write about them. Jean Henri wanted to know more than the books could tell him and had more questions to ask than the teacher could answer.

Because the boy was so interested in all living things he was invited to help care for the flower beds in the teacher's garden. There he found little snails, tiny yellow and pink ones, and white and brown. He thought them so pretty that he went again and again to look at them. Some of the loveliest he caught and cared for so that he might keep on enjoying and studying them.

Many other things Jean Henri studied and learned while he was at school, things that were not yet printed in books. On an alder tree he discovered a beetle of such beautiful blue that he thought it made the sky look pale. On some grassy places he found locusts, spreading their wings into fans of lovely hues, some red, others blue. He never tired of watching the bees under the currant bush, and when they swarmed he enjoyed the "russet smoke" he said they made, hovering near their hives.

All these insects, the beetle and the locusts and the bees, the snails and other little animals in the garden he studied day after day.

When Jean Henri returned to his family they had decided that besides calves and sheep they would raise ducks. "Henri will take care of them," they said. Henri was very happy to do that for more reasons than one. He liked to take care of the ducks because he enjoyed watching them waddle to the brook on their webbed feet, to see them paddling in the water, and it was fun to coax them out and bring them back home again, while he carried the little tired ones in a basket.

The other reason why he liked his new task was that it required he spend much time sitting by the water side while his charges went bathing and paddling about, and that gave him opportunity to watch the little creatures that live in the water.

One day he discovered how interesting were the ways of tadpoles, the frogs' babies. Another day he

watched a big black salamander and imagined it was
the big black dragon the story books told about.

On one of his visits he saw something glimmer in
a little cove in the brook. "Walk along very gently,"
he said to himself, "lie flat on the ground to look."
He stayed a long time quietly looking, for he learned
that the little cove was the home of some minnows.
They seemed to like very much the caverns made by
the twisted roots of the alder trees, for they stayed
right there and did not swim away.

Because they had scarlet throats he named them
"red-necktied minnows." He thought how pretty
they were, and how interesting, clustering side by
side, their heads turned against the stream, puffing
their cheeks in and out, rinsing their mouths without stopping. Suddenly a leaf fell from the tree
above and they all disappeared in a flash.

Henri's family was very poor and there were no
birthday parties or holiday picnics or sight-seeing
trips, or any of the many other kinds of entertainment that amuse many boys and girls. But he did
not ever miss all that. He enjoyed his life so much
that even the hardest days seemed like celebrations
to him. Every day he learned something new about
the wonders of the world of animal life.

When he grew up he made ever more careful studies of the many little creatures that had interested him as a boy. He lived to be a very old man, greatly beloved, and was one of the world's greatest naturalists. What he had learned through looking and thinking all his long life he wrote down. Book after book he wrote, about flies and spiders, and moths and butterflies, about beetles and snails and all the other little creatures he had studied, so that boys and girls, and men and women might enjoy the knowledge he had gained.

When someone asked Fabre whether he believed in God he said, "I see him in all things everywhere." The longer he lived the better he knew what the song in the Bible means that begins, "O Lord God, how wonderful is thy name in all the earth."

A LITTLE RED PURSE

A BUSINESS trip was taking Edward's father through the nearby city, where an uncle had his home. "I'll take you with me," he promised Edward, "for a day's visit with your cousins, and I'll put you on the train for home the next day, when I shall have to travel on."

Edward had not been on trains very often, and it always made him feel very important to be preparing for such a journey. When grown people went on journeys, Edward had found, they often brought presents to boys and girls on their return. That gave him an idea. As he bade good-bye to his mother he called back to his little sister, "I'll bring you something, something very nice, Mary, see if I don't!"

That day in the city was one Edward remembered for a long time. He went to the zoo with his cousins and to the amusement park, where he rode on roller coasters and on the merry-go-round. They had supper in a cafeteria, where all the food was in sight, and his aunt had let him choose whatever he pleased. In the evening he treated his cousins and the boys of the neighborhood, with whom he had played—took them to the corner store where they all had ice cream cones.

The next afternoon his father put him on the train for home. "You won't forget to get off, will you?" he called into the window, just as the train was pulling out, and "Have you any car fare?" "Yes, Father," Edward answered, with the train already in motion, "I've got just a dime left."

At first there were many interesting city sights to see through the train windows, then dairy farms, with cows grazing. The open country later was not quite so interesting. The news and candy man came. "I'll buy myself a chocolate bar," thought Edward and then remembered that he had only his car fare in his purse.

Time passed slowly. Edward began counting the telegraph poles which the train passed. His father had once told him there were thirty-two in a mile. After several miles he tired of that game and leaned back to think and to doze.

Then, with a start, he remembered for the first time since he had left home the promise he had made little Mary. And his pocket money was spent! "I'm a good one," he thought. "She will be so disappointed when I come back without that present."

Much disgusted with his thoughtlessness, and because he could not think of anything else to do, Edward went to get a drink from the fountain at the other end of the car. While he was drawing the water, what should he see, lying beside the drain of the fountain, in the corner, but a silver quarter! What extraordinary luck! It was always fun to find money, but this find seemed too good to be true.

The stores won't be closed when I get home," thought Edward, "and I'll buy Sister a purse yet. That's what little girls like, I noticed, purses to dangle on their arms, even when they haven't any money in them."

His pleasant plans were shattered by the quick thought, "I must try to find the owner of this quarter!" Edward's father and mother had taught him not to rest content until he had tried his best to return to the loser anything he found. So he asked the people sitting near whether they had lost the money. None of them had, and they could not think who the owner might be. As Edward went down the aisle of the train to ask the other passengers he could not help thinking, "I hope the loser won't be among them either." "No," they each said, "not mine!"

When the conductor came along Edward asked him, "Do you know of anyone who lost this money? I've asked all the people in this car." "No, I don't," he answered, patting the boy on the shoulder, "you keep it, Sonny." "Hooray!" said Edward to himself, "now I can get the purse."

The train pulled into his station. As Edward was getting off a man and a woman from the next car were alighting too, with a little girl, who was crying. "I've lost my quarter," Edward heard her wail. Her mother answered, "It's too late to look for it, dear!"

"Will I have to give up that quarter after all?" Edward asked himself. He quickly stepped up to the little girl with a "Here's your quarter. I found it in my car." No sooner had Edward handed over the money than he thought, "Maybe it isn't hers! Why was I so quick about giving it to her?" But he knew that he had not really acted too rashly.

"She probably had a drink while walking through my car," he reflected, "laid down her quarter and forgot it. Anyway, she lost a quarter and I didn't, so it's more hers than mine."

The little girl was so happy to have the money that she would have forgotten to say "Thank you"

61

if her mother had not reminded her. "I guess it's good-bye to Mary's purse," Edward thought ruefully, as the little girl walked away smiling.

Would he really have to go home without the purse? What else could he do but go home without it? Edward got out his dime to board the street car for home, when he had an inspiration. "I could walk that distance, even if it is pretty far. I've walked as far as that before. Mother won't worry because she doesn't know whether I'm coming on this train or the one the next hour. Maybe they have purses in that ten-cent store over there." They did have purses, and Edward bought a shiny red patent leather one for Mary.

It was a long trudge home, and Edward dragged his feet rather wearily for the last blocks, but he got home before his mother had reason to worry about any tardiness.

Mary was so pleased with the little red purse that her mother had to take her for a walk that evening so that there might be occasion to carry it and opportunity to show it to a little playmate in the next block.

Edward felt very happy when he noticed how much his little sister enjoyed the gift. "I knew she would like it," he said proudly to his mother, "but I didn't think she would care so much as all that for it." The next time he went on a journey, he decided, he would not let himself run into any danger of spending all his money on himself.

"BLESS GRANDFATHER"

EVER since he could remember young Peter had closed his evening prayers with a petition for blessings upon all the members of the family, always ending with, "And God bless Grandfather, Amen." Then he had fallen asleep almost as quickly as his head touched the pillow and everything was forgotten until another day.

One Sunday evening the closing sentence of his prayer echoed in Peter's mind: "And God bless Grandfather!" Something stirred in his memory. "Mother," he said, "Miss Brown said in Sunday-school to-day that it isn't enough just to say our prayers. God can't listen to them if we don't care enough about what we say to be willing to help him make the prayer come true." "Miss Brown is quite right, I should say," answered Peter's mother.

"And God bless Grandfather,"—the words still echoed in Peter's mind. "I'm afraid," he said to himself, "I haven't helped God very much about that!" As he drowsed off to sleep he was promising himself, though rather hazily, that somehow he would try to help God bless Grandfather.

The next morning there was the usual hurry and bustle to be off to school. Peter was already out of the gate when he remembered that his mother had often urged him to give a good-bye greeting to Grandfather, who sat in his wheel-chair all day. Peter began to excuse himself: "I won't take time to go back now, but I'll surely remember to-morrow."

Then his resolution came to mind. He ran back to the house and called into the old man's window, "Good-bye, Grandpa, have a good day." "Good-bye, Sonny, good-bye," returned the old man cheerily, though he hardly looked up from his paper.

"I don't suppose it made so very much difference to him," thought Peter, as he retraced his steps toward school, "but Mother says nobody likes being overlooked."

That morning there were lessons in manual training. Peter was glad, for he loved making things. At various times he had brought home book ends for his father, a flower stand for his mother, and many interesting things for himself. On this day the teacher had offered the boys a choice of articles to be made and Peter was thinking hard. He finally decided he would make another book-shelf for his own room. "I get new books right along," he thought, "and the shelf Father gave me is almost full."

He was about to express his choice to the teacher when he remembered hearing his mother explain to his father how Grandfather liked to keep all the old magazines and newspapers in his room. "It is hard to keep the room tidy," his mother had said, "but old folks usually dislike parting with anything that has interested them." "As long as I started out to remember Grandfather to-day," thought Peter, "I might as well keep it up."

So he forgot his own book-shelf for the time being and began work on a magazine stand for his grandfather.

It was a very proud Peter who, some weeks later, brought home the finished product. But Grandfather was still more proud. "Put it right here, by my chair," he directed, "and then I'll be having all these papers handy that I want to read again."

Often when his friends came to call the old man would show them something he had been reading and then he would be heard to say, "My grandson made that stand for me. Smart chap, that boy!" or "Thinking of his Granddaddy when he made that,

—a great youngster." One suspected there was even more pride in the grandson's thoughtfulness than in the handiwork that showed his skill.

One day Peter heard his mother say to his father, "Grandpa lives from mail time to mail time rather than from meal time to meal time, and that is strange for he does not get so very many letters. He enjoys the most ordinary postcard and studies it over and over."

"It is the habit of a lifetime to watch for the mail," Peter's father replied. "He used to have so many letters to read and answer every day. And everyone enjoys being remembered."

"If just a postcard gives Grandpa so much pleasure," thought Peter, "I will send him one every day when I'm out on the farm." Vacation days were very full and Peter did not write as often as he had planned, but he remembered to mail a number of cards to his grandfather, and to include greetings for him in the letters to his parents.

The old man was particularly pleased with a message that told of meeting an old friend of the family's who had said to Peter, "Your Granddaddy was the best fisherman in this county in his day! My, the catches that man used to make." Peter's mother wrote him that his grandfather had chuckled all day over that, and had told bits of stories of his experiences as a fisherman.

One evening after his return home Peter heard an old friend commiserating with his grandfather over the hardships of old age.

"Yes," agreed Peter's grandfather, "in many ways it isn't easy. But my family says I have earned my rest, and they seem to enjoy looking after me. Even the boy. Boys are apt to forget, but he's a great comfort to me. I guess the Bible is right when it says 'In the evening it shall be light.' The evening of my life is very happy."

Peter felt proud but also ashamed. "To think," he said to himself, "that the little I do for him makes such a difference!" And that night when he prayed "God bless Grandfather!" those words really meant, "Thanks for a chance to help bless Grandfather!" for Peter had a very thankful feeling in his heart.

ONE SABBATH DAY

ONE Sabbath morning in Capernaum, when Jesus came into the synagogue and sat down among the people as was his custom, the ruler of the synagogue beckoned to him. He handed him the scroll, and asked Jesus to read the scripture lesson, and to share his understanding of it with the congregation.

The Bible does not say what Jesus read on this morning, but it tells us that as he read his hearers felt in the familiar words a glory and a power and a challenge they had never known before. He was not reading as one merely fulfilling the law which said that the lesson must be read on the Sabbath morning. His reading showed that he was seeing great truth in these Scriptures, and that he was eager to talk with the people about it.

When he had finished Jesus handed the scroll to the attendant and began to speak. Perhaps he spoke, as he had done before, of God's plan that all people have liberty, that they be free from fear and ignorance and hate, that they might see what is good to do and gain the courage and the strength to do it as God's children. "Now is the time for all this to come about," said Jesus, "the acceptable year of the Lord has come."

He spoke with power and authority. Words about liberty for the bruised and sight for the blind and release for the captives were not just beautiful words to Jesus, but they meant to him a great task he would stake his life to fulfil, a mission God had laid upon him as his son; they told the compassion for people that filled his own soul.

The listeners had followed his words with rapt attention. When Jesus finished they said to each other, "Is this Jesus of Nazareth, the son of Joseph the carpenter? He speaks with such grace and power and understanding and with so much authority!"

Among those who attended services that morning was a man who was not in his right mind. He was spoken of as a demoniac because it was believed, according to the explanation of those days, that a demon, an unclean spirit, was in him.

This man ran forward to Jesus. Excited by the interest and strong feeling in the group, he cried out with a loud voice, "Ah, what have I to do with thee, Jesus of Nazareth? I know thee, who thou art, the Holy one of God."

Jesus, seeing the man's great need, spoke to him

very calmly, as to an unclean spirit, "Hold thy peace and be quiet and come out of him."

To everyone's astonishment the raving man grew instantly quiet, his face became calm and peaceful, and he was like other people.

Again the people said to each other, "Jesus speaks with so much power and authority,—even the unclean spirits obey him."

When the meeting was over everyone went home very quietly, according to the law of the Sabbath. But they were thinking hard. There would be liberty for captives, sight for the blind, Jesus believed. And he did not mean just blindness of the eyes, and he was not thinking of iron chains. They would like to be with him more, they thought, and learn of him how this might come about, this clear sight and this liberty; they would like to gain strength from his presence, who was courageous and unafraid and wise, that they might know and do God's will.

The Bible story does not tell what they said and planned as they came home but the happenings of the evening help us imagine that.

One man, who could hardly wait to return to his family, we can hear saying to his wife as he came into the door, "Jesus of Nazareth spoke in the synagogue this morning. Everything people praise about him is true. There is power in him, and love, and courage, and mastery of life. He made the demoniac well. To-night, as soon as the sun is down, I want to take our son to him. Perhaps Jesus can help him too."

There was a man who had done a wrong he thought about so much day and night that he could not sleep. He was so unhappy that he thought life was not worth living any more. That man may have been saying to himself as he went along, "I will go after sundown to listen to Jesus again,—he says God is a God of love,—perhaps I will yet find peace for my soul and forgiveness."

All the Sabbath day the people stayed very quietly in their homes, but as soon as the sun was set they came forth.

They hastened to Simon Peter's home, where Jesus was visiting with Simon Peter and his family and friends. When Jesus heard voices outside speaking his name, he went out and saw great groups of people waiting for him, and more and more coming, all troubled about something. On many he laid his hands in healing. Others asked him questions and he counselled with them. He did not let anyone go away without some help, some comfort or confidence, or new understanding or strength.

The father could go home with his son, once troubled and sick, now joyous beside him. Jesus had noticed the man so greatly troubled about the wrong he had done, how sorry he was, and he talked with him. The man went away with new hope, thinking, "God is my father, he will yet give me a chance to live as his child, and I will."

Proud people who had come merely to look on, to be entertained, went away ashamed and humble. They had the feeling that the clear eyes of Jesus had seen them sinful as they were, and weak as they had not known themselves to be. All sensed the power and authority, the courage and love that were in him.

The people asked Jesus to stay with them all the time, but he said, "I must preach the good tidings of the Kingdom of God to the other cities also, for therefore was I sent."

Then he went into the desert, for he wanted time and quiet to think alone and to pray. The next morning he went out to meet his disciples, and they went with him as he taught and healed the people who were needing him.

THE SISTINE MADONNA

SEVERAL centuries ago there lived in Italy a young painter named Raphael, who used his great talent, his brushes and paint, to help the people in their worship. One day it was decided that the monastery of San Sisto needed a picture to beautify the chapel where the monks went to pray, and Raphael was called upon to paint it.

The madonna and child was chosen as the subject. A great scaffold was built against the wall, and Raphael came to the chapel every day to paint the picture. For three months he worked, as the figures of the mother and child, the adoring saints and angels, each day became more like his ideas of them.

When the painting was finished it drew the eyes of all who entered the chapel and its beauty and meaning exalted the spirit of all beholders.

The Prince of Saxony, who was travelling all over Europe, one day stopped to pay the monastery a visit. He came into the chapel and was startled by the beauty of the picture of the mother and child. There were the soft blue mantle and the red tunic of the madonna, and the gorgeous robes of the saints, but it was not these which made the picture so beautiful to him.

The look of mystery in the mother's eyes, and of willingness to sacrifice her dearest, if need be,—it was that most of all which impressed him so greatly. And the deep eyes of the baby in her arms reflected, he felt, the soul of him who was to be the saviour of the world. The mother and the child, as they seemed to float toward him on the clouds, were very real indeed to the prince.

He resolved he must have the picture for the people in the big city of Dresden, in his home in faraway Saxony. The monks did not want to give up their treasure, but year after year the prince continued to urge them to let him have it, with offers of more and more money.

After forty long years of persuasion, when the prince had long become king of his country, the monks finally decided to let him have the picture. They did it only on condition that the king would have a copy made for their chapel, as nearly like Raphael's work as possible.

So the "Sistine Madonna," as the painting had come to be named, after the chapel which had been its home, was very carefully packed. Then it was sent on its journey to Dresden, where the people were eagerly waiting for the picture now spoken of by many as "the most beautiful in the world."

When the big box in which the painting had travelled arrived in Dresden it was taken to the palace and carried right to the very room where the king's throne stood. Many stood about to watch the unwrapping of the art treasure their king had desired so long.

The place in the throne room where the lighting was found to be best was the very wall where the great golden throne stood. So the king impatiently shoved against the throne with his foot and said, "Make room for the great Raphael!"

Raphael's picture of the Madonna and Child did not remain on that wall very long. It was considered too beautiful to be kept in a place no more accessible to all people than is a king's throne room. Therefore it was taken to the Royal Art Gallery, where thousands of people go every year to see great paintings. A room in the gallery was set aside for the Sistine Madonna alone.

Now scholars and merchants, rich and poor, young and old, travellers from all over the world, go to that room in Dresden to see this painting. All stand reverent before its beauty and before the look of deep devotion in the faces of the mother and child.

A SHERIFF WHO LOVED
PRISONERS

JOHN HOWARD lived in England, in a beautiful house out in the country, many years ago. All who knew him thought of him as a good man, for he loved his church, he loved his family, and he loved his neighbors.

He loved his neighbors so much that he used some of his money to help them build better homes. Many of the poor farmers in his county were able, because of his help, to tear down their old ramshackle houses and build nice new cottages. He built and maintained schools for all the children of the neighborhood and he safeguarded the health of the people in the village by providing for the best kind of sanitation.

A man who did so much good in the world might have been tempted to say to himself, "I've done just about all that I ought to do." It is possible that John Howard would have come to say that except for the fact that his neighbors thought so much of him that they elected him their sheriff.

In the county in which John Howard lived there

was a very old county jail, for which, as sheriff, he became responsible, and for the prisoners in it. The first time he went into this jail he found that the prisoners were starving. No one was responsible for providing them with food, and they were not given work by means of which they might earn what they needed.

When he asked the people of the county to supply provisions for the prisoners some of them protested very strongly. "Of course not," was their answer. "It was their fault, the prisoners' very own fault, that they got into jail,—why should we care whether they have food or not?"

John Howard was very much disappointed. What could he do next, he wondered, to get help for his prisoners? Then he had an idea. He hit upon a plan which, he thought, was bound to be successful.

"I know how I will get around my righteous neighbors!" he said to himself, as he set out upon a journey through the neighboring counties, to inspect the jails there. "When I return I will tell the people of my county how much better their neighbors treat the prisoners, and then they will be much ashamed."

His scheme did not work. To his horror he found the other jails even worse.

That little jaunt through the neighboring counties, and the discoveries he made, changed the whole life of John Howard. He was no longer a young man,—he had reached an age when most people do not begin new adventures, and, besides, he was not in good health. Nevertheless, he decided he would visit all the jails in England and on the continent of Europe to learn whatever he might about them.

He began his travels with some hope of finding good conditions in the jails somewhere. "These French prisons are bad," he would think while in France, "probably the German ones will be better." When he got to Germany he thought, "These German prisons are very bad, perhaps when I get to Norway or Sweden I will see better ones." But finally he gave up all hope, for as he visited country after country he found that everywhere the prisons were terrible.

In not one of them were the prisoners provided with food. Inmates of prisons kept from starving only if they had enough money of their own to buy provisions or had relatives or friends who could afford time and money to supply them.

In some of the prisons he found terrible diseases raging. In most of them there was no bedding and the prisoners had to sleep on the cold floor. Because of such conditions many prisoners died shortly after being imprisoned.

"This is all the more wrong and all the more sad," said John Howard, "because some of the people in prison have done nothing that was so particularly bad." He wrote in his journal that some were poor people who through illness or other misfortune had come to owe someone money, for according to the laws of that time you could be thrown into prison if you owed anyone a debt. Many were in trouble because they had never had a decent chance to live uprightly.

Often prisoners had to stay in jail long after their term was up, because they could not afford to pay the jailer's fees, for in those days the prisoners were charged by the jailer for his supposed services to them.

John Howard always kept a journal in his pocket into which he wrote accounts of whatever he saw in the prisons. This journal told of his experiences as far north as Sweden, as far south as Italy, and in all the countries between. When he got home he sat down to read over his notes and to remember what he had seen. Then he wrote a book about it all. He also wrote articles for the magazines and sent many letters to all parts of the country.

Soon people all over England, people even who had never before given prisons a thought, were heard to be talking about them, were heard to be saying to each other, "We ought to be ashamed of our prisons, oughtn't we?" And a good many went so far as to say, "We will help John Howard do something about it!"

Because of John Howard's information and influence Parliament made a law abolishing jailer's fees and providing for more healthful living in the prisons. He had copies of this law printed at his own expense and sent to every jailer in England. Many lazy jailers did not obey the law,—merely threw the notice of it into their waste-baskets—but much good came of it in many places.

Of course, many people could not change their ways of thinking so quickly, and they still opposed John Howard in his enterprises for the good of the people in the jails. "If we treat bad people too nicely," they said, "they will never feel sorry for their sins." But John Howard had not read his Bible in vain. "Don't you know," he said to his opponents, "that Jesus told us to love our enemies and reminded us that God lets his sun shine on the evil as well as the good? And don't you remember his saying, 'Let him who is without sin cast the first stone'?" John Howard knew that punishment without love and thoughtfulness could not be expected to help anyone grow better.

He continued to travel, hundreds and hundreds of miles, in every part of Europe, and everywhere he called the attention of good people to the very evil way in which they treated the people who had been imprisoned.

Everybody came to know about John Howard and his work. When he went to Rome the Pope asked to see him. After a long and pleasant conversation, when the visitor rose to go, the Pope said, "You probably do not believe that a Pope can bless anyone; but the blessings of an old man will do you no harm." Then he laid his hands upon John Howard's head and asked God's blessing upon him.

His last journey led him to southern Russia, where he went to inspect the military hospitals, reported to be in a deplorable condition. There he died from a cold, contracted while riding a horse through a terrible storm to get to the bedside of a girl whom he had befriended.

He had asked that only a sun dial be placed over his grave but his friends insisted on raising a large monument above it. On the marble there was engraved in the Russian language, under the name John Howard, and the date of his death, 1790, this beautiful inscription:

"Whoever thou art, thou standest at the tomb of thy friend."

Some of the reforms he desired have not been accomplished even to-day, although it is a long time since John Howard lived. In our country there are very many prisons and reform schools of which we should be thoroughly ashamed, places where people are likely to become worse rather than better members of society. But all prisons are more decent than they used to be, because of this one man. Christian people have learned just a little about showing love and understanding even to people who have done wrong.

PIERRE AND MARIE CURIE

WHEN Pierre Curie and his wife Marie went holidaying, away from their work in Paris, it was always on their bicycles or on foot, for then they could easily stop to pick the water daffodils they saw along the streams; they could watch the ways of turtles and beetles, or perhaps study the trees and the ferns by the roadside. Through forest and field, along the countryside and by the seashore they would roam, studying, observing, appreciating nature.

The Curies enjoyed their vacations greatly, but they were never sorry to return home to work again. For though the beauty and the variety of outdoors gave them much delight, greater still was the joy both Pierre and Marie Curie found in studying metals and crystals, in learning more about electricity and magnetism, in searching for new knowledge about all the sort of things in which the scientists we know as physicists are interested.

The new knowledge they gained helped many people, and the Curies became famous, but the fame their success brought them did not impress them greatly. When Pierre Curie was offered the distinction of the Legion of Honor he refused to accept it, for he said, "A scientist's work should be done for the love of it. An eye to fame and glory would cheapen its quality."

While they were searching together for new knowledge it happened that Pierre and Marie Curie made a discovery for which all the world owes them special thanks. It was not a discovery that came by accident. It was not one which could have come in that way.

The story of the discovery began when one day Marie Curie decided she would try to find out more about certain mysterious substances which give forth heat and light. Her interest was very great,—the subject fascinated her. She studied many books to see what others had learned about these substances before her, and found it was very little indeed that anyone knew, that she would have to do the work of finding out almost from the beginning.

Pierre Curie became so interested in the new problem that he discontinued his own experiments and joined his wife in tracing down the cause of this wonderful glow which had aroused her curiosity.

The place where they had been working was not

large enough for all the instruments and vessels and tanks they needed for their work, and they could not afford a real laboratory, that is, a specially built and furnished scientist's work place. So the Curies moved their equipment into an old abandoned storeroom across the way.

There was only an earthen floor, the roof leaked, the stove was too small to keep the place warm, and the soot blew in through the window cracks. But the old storeroom became a very happy place in spite of these difficulties and Pierre and Marie Curie did not notice the shortcomings except in some very discouraged times, when cold or dirt or lack of room handicapped them greatly.

Day after day they worked, almost feverish in their eagerness to find out just what it was that gave forth this heat and light, where it could be found, how to extract the substance, what it would do. After a time they learned what substance it was and that it could be found in the raw material known as pitchblende. The problem was now to get some of it pure, out of the raw material.

They learned of a mine in Austria where it would be possible to get large quantities of the pitchblende they wanted. It was expensive, and tons of it were needed in order to get from it just a very little of the valuable element for which they were searching, but somehow the Curies made it possible to spare from their meagre teacher salaries the money they needed.

Soon the place was full of great vessels of boiling stuff, Marie and Pierre Curie going about shifting, transferring, or stirring with a great iron bar.

Both spent all possible hours of the day in their laboratory and sometimes they worked at night also. The loving old doctor grandfather played nursemaid to the little daughter in order that the mother might be more free to spend her days at work with the father.

At times Pierre and Marie Curie would slip into the laboratory after dark, just to enjoy the sight of the bottles and capsules on the shelves, full of the gleaming substance which had been extracted from the masses of raw material in the great vats and tanks all about. Marie Curie said that the glowing of the shining stuff in the darkness made her think of fairy lights.

It was a more and more difficult task to separate the element they sought from its compounds, and therefore, as the work came nearer and nearer to completion, it became more and more exciting.

Finally, after several years of hard work, on a May morning in 1898, when they had worked all night, they found that their great day had come, for Marie Curie held in her hand their new discovery, a little of that very precious element radium.

Radium is ever and ever so much more precious than gold or diamonds, an element not only beautiful to see but one that has in it a power which seems almost like magic to help in the healing of diseases.

All over the world people were happy over the discovery, and great fame came to Pierre and Marie Curie. They kept on learning more about radium, the things it can be made to do, the ways it works. Doctors learned of the new discovery and soon suffering people everywhere were helped through radium. In the factories of Europe and America where radium was extracted and where radium appliances were made for the hospitals, the work was done in the way the Curies had discovered and had made known for anyone to copy.

Through all this use of their findings the Curie family might have become very wealthy. When Pierre and Marie Curie were asked about their income from the discovery, and when friends suggested ways of making money out of it, they seemed surprised that money should be mentioned, and said, "Radium is not to enrich anyone. It is for all people."

They kept on living as simply as before, humble before all the praise that came to them, happy that they had been able to do a service to mankind through the work they loved. Their favorite way to celebrate a holiday was still an excursion into the country, where Pierre Curie taught his young daughter to love nature and to inquire into its mysteries, just as his father had taught him.

When at a later time Pierre Curie and his wife were again urged to make money out of their discovery they stood by their decision, that "Radium is not to enrich anyone. It is for all people."

A SLAVE WHO THOUGHT HE WAS FREE

(FOR OLDER BOYS AND GIRLS)

You will not find all of this story in the Bible although it is about the Lord Jesus and about a young man whom he knew. But if the story is not recorded in the Scriptures you may be sure that it is true nevertheless, for it has happened many a time in the past, and in some way or other happens many times even nowadays.

JESUS was travelling the paths of the earth, helping people in trouble, teaching them to live courageously and in God's presence as did he. His disciples went with him to follow him wherever he would go. There were many others who followed him part of the time and wanted to stay with him always, but somehow they did not. Something was in the way, in every case.

There was a rich young ruler who had learned to love Jesus. He listened from afar and wished much to be a disciple. Now, as many times before, he was standing at the edge of a crowd that was gathered about the Master. "To-day," he thought, "I will have the courage to go to Jesus and say 'I will follow thee,' for I am ready to leave my home and go where he goes, if he will have me. I want to live the life for others that Jesus lives." But when he said that the young ruler did not yet know what he was saying.

He came nearer, to join a group standing close about Jesus, some talking with the Master, others waiting to hear him address the multitude. Beside the young ruler stood two other young men, whom he knew, Joses and Barnabas, also waiting to hear Jesus.

Barnabas said, "Jesus is wise and strong and good. In him is life. But I cannot follow him, for my friends do not believe in him. They make fun of me for caring so much about the things Jesus says and does. One cannot go against one's friends!"

The young ruler looked with compassion on Barnabas beside him as he thought, "Barnabas cannot do what he wants to do! I am happy I am not bound. I am glad that I am free. Barnabas is really a slave, a slave to the opinions of his friends."

Barnabas's companion, Joses, answered, "My friends don't bother me. They respect my judgment and accept my decisions. And they'd better, for I don't ask them to agree. But I am not ready to give up my dream to be great in my profession, for I have a good start. Some things I need to do for advancement's sake Jesus would not approve, but I have to do them."

On Joses too the young ruler looked with pity, as he said to himself, "Joses cannot do what he wants to do! I am happy I am not bound. I am glad that I am free. Joses is really a slave, a slave to his ambition."

Just then he heard a man say to Jesus, "I will follow thee when my father shall be no more among the living. When he has died I will do what the voice in me commands. But my father would not approve of my changing my way of life and therefore I cannot follow thee now."

And again the young ruler said to himself, "I am glad I am not bound. I am happy I am free. That man, too, is really a slave, he is a slave to his family."

Then Jesus spoke to the multitude, and the young ruler loved him more than ever. He was fired with the desire, as before, to be with the Master and to learn to live a life that would count forever. Therefore when Jesus had finished speaking and the multitude had dispersed, he came forward and asked, "Master, what shall I do to inherit eternal life? I have observed the commandments from my youth!"

When Jesus saw him he loved him and felt wistful over the sacrifice he must ask, for the young man too seemed to care for something else more than he did for the Kingdom of Heaven. He was very wealthy. "Sell what you have," said Jesus, "and give it to the poor, and then come and follow me."

The young ruler was startled. He had not thought of such a thing and he looked at Jesus in hurt surprise. "Sell all I have?" he seemed to ask. "Not have the things money has bought for me and the power it gives? Not be sure of the next day's food?" To be no better off than his father's employes? Sorrowfully he bowed his head and slowly he walked away.

Jesus looked after him sadly. For he saw that the young ruler was bound and not free, that he did not live as he wanted, for he, too, was a slave, a slave to his possessions.

THE PARABLE OF THE TREES

This is a make-believe story, recorded in that old chronicle of history, the Book of the Judges. It was written at a time when the leader of the children of Israel was a man quite unworthy of such rank among them. The story is known as the "parable of the trees."

THE trees once upon a time decided that they wanted someone to be ruler above them, someone to be their guide and king. So they went to the olive tree, whose fruit is used to feed the hungry, to produce oil for the anointing of kings, for sacrifices in the temple and to soothe the pain of the wounded.

The trees said to the olive tree, "Reign thou over us!" The leaves of the olive tree glistened in the sunlight in proud humility as he said, "Should I leave off bringing forth fruit through which I help serve God and man, and go to be promoted over the trees?" And he shook his leafy head to say "No!"

Then the trees said to the fig tree, "Come thou and reign over us!" But the fig tree said to them,

95

humbly proud in being honored by their trust, "Should I forsake my sweetness and the good fruit which the people want for food, and go to be promoted over the trees? And truly, I am not great enough to reign over you." Then the fig tree rustled his leaves to say "No" also.

The trees next petitioned the vine, whose fruit is used for the refreshment of the people, and they said, "Come thou and reign over us!" And the vine said, "Should I leave off bringing forth fruit and go to be promoted over the trees? Besides, I am not great enough to be your ruler," and his leaves rustled "No," as he wafted the perfume of the grape blossoms on the breeze.

Finally, in an unthinking moment, the trees said to the bramble-bush, the scraggly, useless bramble-bush, "Come thou, and reign over us!" The bramble-bush, who had nothing to do but think much of himself, spread his short branches as far as he might, puffed his leaves to stand very stiffly, and said, in a very pompous manner, "You have chosen well indeed, to ask me to reign over you. If indeed you anoint me king over you, then put your trust in my shadow, and if not, let fire come out of the brambles and devour the cedars of Lebanon!"

THE PARABLE OF THE TREES

The majestic, stately cedars of Lebanon looked puzzled, and all the other trees stood very quiet in their bewilderment. The bramble-bush was so proud in his dream of himself as a great and powerful king, that he did not notice any lack of homage. He did not notice how ashamedly some of the trees were hanging their heads over their thoughtlessness in addressing him, and how some were shaking with laughter to think that the bramble-bush had taken them so seriously.

It is said that the bramble-bush has never stopped being proud, that it has never entered his mind to realize he is not a king, and never was a king, but always only a bramble-bush.

HAMILTON AND JEFFERSON

THIS story happened in the days when the Declaration of Independence was written, in the time when our government was being established, when men wore three-cornered hats, and shiny buckles on their shoes.

Thomas Jefferson, who wrote the Declaration of Independence, was the first Secretary of State, and Alexander Hamilton was the Secretary of the Treasury.

They were both great men, Jefferson and Hamilton. But they never worked together, even though they sat side by side in President Washington's cabinet. When Hamilton voted "Yes" on any question, Jefferson would be practically sure to vote "No"; when Jefferson would say *"This* is the thing we should do," Hamilton could be depended upon to say, "No, *that* is what ought to be done."

They did not disagree because they wanted to oppose each other, but because they had such very different ways of looking at life, these two great men. They both loved their country, but their ideas about the best way to serve her varied greatly.

Jefferson wanted all citizens to have an opportunity to help govern the country and to express their opinions about its affairs. Hamilton was a man of masterful ways, and he wanted all power in the hands of just a few people.

Jefferson was a rich man but his heart was with the poor. Everything he did was designed to help the poor pioneers who were clearing the forests and cultivating the land in the outposts of American civilization. Hamilton was a poor man, but he lived among the rich. Everything he did was meant to give to the wealthier classes of the cities a stronger hold on the American government.

The more Jefferson and Hamilton differed the more there grew bitterness between their followers. Therefore the followers of Jefferson were much surprised at something they saw when they visited their leader in his Virginia home, Monticello.

In the great reception hall a life-size bust of Hamilton adorned the mantelpiece and looked down upon every visitor who came to talk with Jefferson about politics and government. How could Jefferson so honor the man who was his chief opponent, who spoke so critically of him? Jefferson's friends could not understand. "Whatever makes you do that?" they asked him.

"Why shouldn't I?" asked Jefferson in return. "Hamilton is a great man who has done much for our country, and I honor him as a great man, even if I don't agree with him."

Jefferson's followers did not yet understand. They were inclined to dislike decidedly anyone with whom they disagreed strongly, and they thought everyone did that. In Jefferson's home, standing before the statue of his chief opponent Hamilton, they would say to themselves, wonderingly, "Time after time we get together here, work as hard as we can with Jefferson to keep Hamilton's plans from coming to pass, and there stands Jefferson telling about the good in Hamilton."

They could not understand. They never quite understood.

But if they lived long enough they lived to find that Hamilton's followers had joined them in appreciating Jefferson.

When he was quite an old man, after serving two terms as President of the United States, Jefferson lost most of his property. For a time it even seemed that he would be turned out of Monticello, the home he had worked years and years to build and which he had loved all his life. Then the people of the country started a fund to save Monticello for its master, and later they bought it to perpetuate his memory among the new generations.

The money needed came from everywhere. Among those who helped save Jefferson's home there were some who had been outstanding among the followers of his old enemy Hamilton. Perhaps they had the feeling of one old-time bitter opponent, President Adams. When the reasons for disagreement were no longer so important and were possibly forgotten, Adams wrote to a friend, "I have always loved Jefferson and I always shall."

At any rate, Hamilton's followers were seeing the greatness in Jefferson and were glad to do something to show how much they revered him who had had so much respect for all people, regardless of their opinions.

FOR MARGARET KNEW

MARGARET lived on a big boat most of the year, while other little girls were at home and going to school. Her father was captain of a Great Lakes steamer and Margaret wanted to be with him because he was all the family she had. But that was not the only reason. Life on board the ship was so very interesting,—much more interesting, Margaret felt, than life on land.

She liked to watch the sailors at their work and learned herself to climb the highest mast. Sometimes she roamed away down in the hold of the ship and stopped to watch the wheels of the machinery go round and round, or she hung over the railing of the deck, fascinated by the churning, always churning water that sprayed her face as the ship plied its way through the lake.

Homes on land, and especially schools, made Margaret feel shut in. It was enchanting to live between water and sky. When she lived on land she could not watch the ways of the sea-gulls, she did not have the fun of stopping in all the many interesting har-

102

bors where old friends greeted the captain's little daughter as a sailor comrade. One time the boat went all the way down the St. Lawrence river as far as Montreal, where Margaret saw a great ocean-going steamer.

All during the shipping season, and that was from early spring until the ice closed the lakes, Margaret lived this exciting life on the big boat with her father.

You can see that there were not many months when she was on land and going to school. Time and again, although she was acknowledged to be a very bright pupil, Margaret lost her place in her classes and failed of promotion. Finally,—she was a girl of fourteen then,—she lost all interest in her studies, and left school altogether, in spite of her father's wishes. She had not finished the work that would have admitted her to high school.

When she grew up, perhaps strange to say, Margaret became a milliner. She found great pleasure in fitting hats on girls and women, in seeing the customers go out of the store pleased with themselves as they gave a last satisfied glance into her mirror. She was so efficient and understanding that by and by she became manager of a millinery store and found no reason to worry about the education she had failed to get. That is, for a while she did not worry. Then something happened.

Margaret had joined the church, and in the services one Sunday she heard a missionary tell of his work on one of the "islands of the sea," where people needed everything that he could do for them. She listened with almost breathless interest, and found herself wishing she could do something that helped so much to make people happy.

"But I could not be a missionary," she said, excusing herself. "God could not send me, for I have no education." So she gave some money, a large amount for her, and felt that was all she could do, and needed to do.

A few months later Margaret heard another missionary, a physician, tell of his work in another country, a country where there was only one doctor for thousands and thousands of people, and where every other kind of help was needed. The memory of the troubled people he told about gave her mind no peace. She decided she must go to this country herself, to do what she could even if she had not as much schooling as might be desired.

She offered her services to a missionary board, but

was told in reply that others were ahead of her and that her name could not be considered at that time. Margaret knew very well they were only too polite to say her education was not sufficient, that she did not know enough to be of service.

"I may not know enough now," she said to herself, "but I will know enough as soon as that can be."

Determined to get the education she needed, Margaret McKellar went back to school. At the age of twenty-two she had to sit on school benches with young children. As she sat there she feared the boys and girls might laugh at her and she used to pray that they would not make fun of her. When she had finished the work in the grades Margaret went to high school.

After that she took the medical course in Queens University in Canada and completed her school preparation as a doctor of medicine in London, England. Again she offered her services to the mission board of her church and this time they accepted her gladly and sent her to India.

Margaret was now a full-fledged physician and as Doctor McKellar she cared for thousands of sick people in India. Her work grew year by year; after a time she had her own great hospital where she trained nurses who went into the villages and the farther provinces to care for the many who needed their help.

One time, twenty-five years after Margaret Mc-Kellar had first landed in India, the King and Queen of England came for a visit. A great celebration was planned to which Margaret was bidden. There the greatest honor was bestowed upon her that had yet come to a woman of India on any such occasion, for the medal known as the Kaisar-i-Hind medal for service to India was given to her by the Queen.

Someone asked Doctor McKellar, "What did you think when the Queen was pinning the medal on you?" "Oh," she replied, "only one thought came into my mind, and that was of those days when as a grown-up woman I sat in school with boys and girls, when I asked myself over and over, 'Is it worth while?'"

Now, after twenty-five years of service, Margaret McKellar must have smiled when she remembered that she had ever asked, "Is it worth while?"

"BLESSED ARE . . ."

AT the beginning of the last century, when the Middle West was just being settled, the pioneers who came to that region did not have a great variety of food to eat.

The chief food was fish from the rivers and meat which the hunters brought home from forest and prairie. The settlers and their families had to eat fish and game, game and fish, and again fish and game. If they had not grown so hungry from their hard work, felling forests and ploughing prairies, they would have found their meals very monotonous indeed. Even at best they grew weary of the food and welcomed with joy any little addition or change.

They had to make farms and gardens and orchards out of uncultivated prairies and primeval forests, for the Indians who lived there before them were hunters, not farmers and gardeners. No one had been ahead of them planting vegetable gardens or berry patches, or cherry, or plum, or apple orchards. What a difference it would have made if only there had been some apple trees! Then they might have

107

had apple pies, and apple dumplings, and apple sauce and apple fritters to eat! As it was, there were trees, a great many of them, but they were maples and oaks and elms, trees that gave shade to rest in but no fruit to eat.

There was a man from Massachusetts, named Jonathan Chapman, who learned about this difficulty of the early settlers. "I know of something I can do to help them, even if I have no money," he said to himself quite determinedly; and presently he set forth on a journey.

His blue eyes were so mild and his manner so quiet and unassuming that no one would have guessed he had any particular plan or purpose as he travelled along. Sometimes he walked beside, sometimes he sat astride, the old horse that was his companion.

His first destination on the journey west was a town where there were cider mills, a town in the centre of a region of the state of New York known for its many apple orchards. Cider mills make cider out of apples, but they find no use for apple seeds. Jonathan Chapman remembered that, so he sought a mill and asked the owners for permission to take the pressed-out apple pulp full of apple seeds.

The cider-mill owners thought, "What a very queer thing to ask! What can anyone do with so many apple seeds? But why not let him have the stuff if he wants it?" So they gave him the permission he requested. He filled some old coffee sacks with the dry, pressed-out apples, loaded them on his horse, and travelled on.

When he got to Pennsylvania he decided that his horse and he could manage to carry a little more. He found another cider mill, where they let him have all the seeds he cared to take, although they thought, "What a queer-looking fellow he is! His clothes seem to be just gunny sacks with holes cut out for arms and legs. And who ever heard of wearing a tin pan for a hat!" Perhaps they guessed, and perhaps they did not suspect, that he had another use for the pan, for he did his own cooking on the long stretches in his travels where there were not yet many farms or towns.

He arrived in Ohio, which was then quite sparsely settled, and there Jonathan Chapman got a new name. He went about very quietly planting apple seeds in all likely looking places. He planted them beside the roads, in patches of ground not otherwise used, in the corners of meadows and pastures. All day long he planted, travelled, planted some more, until all his seeds were gone.

Not very many people saw him at his work because there were not yet a great many people living there. Those who saw him planting, planting, always planting apple seeds, could not help remembering how he looked, and what he did, and they told others about him. Soon all the region knew the traveller as "Johnnie Appleseed."

It was in 1801, the histories say, that Johnnie Appleseed came to Ohio, when he was possibly twenty-six years old, a young man of medium height, with the straight, long brown hair that may have been an inheritance from an Indian ancestor.

Five years later there is a story of Johnnie drifting down the Ohio river with two canoe loads of apple seeds lashed together, on the way to regions beyond the present state of Ohio to what was then the most western frontier. He was in advance of the great army of western pioneers, raising apple trees before people could miss them. Johnnie Appleseed was going to be ahead of even the pioneers, ahead of the first settlers.

Always barefoot, winter and summer, he journeyed, sometimes on foot, sometimes on rafts he himself had made to carry his freight of apple seeds. Occasionally he looked quite dressed up, for instead of his gunny-sack clothes he would be wearing an old suit he had traded for some apple trees. Always he stopped to plant his seeds, on sunny days and cloudy, in stormy weather and fair.

Johnnie was a religious man and beside the apple seeds he carried Bibles for distribution. Often he stopped to read to friends his favorite chapters from the Scriptures.

Johnnie's apple trees began to grow and to bear fruit through all the Western settlements. Within less than forty years the orchards he had planted covered an area of possibly one hundred square miles. Those orchards were a great delight to him, and he enjoyed going over his old trails to cultivate old tree friends among his early plantings.

Now, everywhere boys and girls could look forward to dinner with anticipation, for there would be apple dumplings or fritters, apple sauce or apple pie. They found that a juicy apple pie can quite well change into a feast what would otherwise be merely a meal. Weary travellers rejoiced to see by the roadside trees laden with red-cheeked or golden apples, offering them refreshment on the journey.

Many people expressed their appreciation to Johnnie for the apples on which they feasted, although great numbers who munched them with enjoyment never knew that they were indebted to him. Everyone treated Johnnie with respect. Even in the War of 1812, when the Indian allies of the enemy slaughtered many white settlers, he was permitted to go among them unmolested.

For forty-six years Johnnie Appleseed had travelled, when a peaceful easy death came to him. After a tramp of twenty miles he had arrived at the home of a friend in Fort Wayne, Indiana. Wearily he sat on the doorstep and was brought bread and milk for his supper. When he had refreshed himself, as twilight was falling, he took out his Bible and read to his hosts from the beatitudes, "Blessed are the merciful, blessed are the meek, blessed are the peacemakers."

Then he lay down, and went to sleep, and in the night he died.

His friends told many interesting memories of kind, old, unassuming Johnnie Appleseed. They liked to recall their last memory of him, as he sat on their doorstep in the dusk, reading, "Blessed are the merciful, blessed are the meek."

A PICK-AND-SHOVEL POET

PASCAL D'ANGELO, fifteen years old, was water-boy for a pick-and-shovel gang building roads in New York state. His home had been in Italy. His birthplace was in the lovely valley where the great poet of antiquity, Ovid, was born, and, who knows, that fact may have had something to do with the future that was coming to Pascal.

Now, for the time being, his home was in a little smoky wooden shack, beside big piles of gravel, quite far away from Italy.

At night when the smoke from the men's cooking was filling the shack and the boy Pascal was waiting for his own pot of soup to get hot, he sometimes sat on the two boards that were his bunk, dreaming. He would recall the great mountains at home in Italy, the picturesque slopes with wild roses beside cool springs, the old ruined castle on the heights where flocks of pigeons always roosted. He would think of the sheep and lambs and the goats which he had herded for the family, and he would remember with great affection the little house in that valley, and the father and mother and brother with whom he had lived there.

He loved Italy. Now he had come to America with his father and a group of friends, and his devotion to his new home, to America, was very deep too. He wanted to be a good American.

However, he did not have much time to think about that, nor to dream about his old home, for the days were very busy. He was helping in a big job of road building. The present task was to dig a road through a hill. Ten hours a day the gang worked. Trucks were driven up, which the workers quickly filled with the sand and earth they had dug or the rock they had blasted away.

The job was the beginning of the years Pascal spent working on highways and railroads in many different states, from Maryland to Illinois, in the North and in the South. He started as water-boy but before long he was given a pick and a shovel too, and then his work was digging, always digging, new road beds, or spreading sand on gravel on the nearly finished roads, or levelling bumpy places in old ones.

All Pascal's gang worked from early morning till late evening, building roads where none had been or making poor ones better. Sometimes they could find no work anywhere and then they would live on their small savings while they went about looking for a livelihood. The members of the gang came to care for each other as if they were members of one family. They planned, in this new country where everything and everyone was strange to them, to stay together, and they tried desperately to work out the plan, to find work at the same jobs.

Hard labor all day long and rest times in tumble-down shanties or in box cars sometimes so broken down that they did not protect from the rain,—that does not sound like a very interesting life for a young man. There was entertainment and some excitement in Pascal's days, however. It came out of a small, half-torn Webster's dictionary which he had bought second-hand for a quarter.

He used it to teach himself the English language, and he made quite a game out of doing that. In fact, he memorized the dictionary, page after page, writing the new words he learned in chalk on the mouldy walls of the box car he lived in, or on the railroad ties along the road he was helping to build.

Soon he could give definitions for very many words which the people about him, who were born in America and had gone to American schools, did not know. His friends would feel triumphant all day if they succeeded in giving him one word for which he could not tell the definition.

One day they thought they had the best of him. They brought five high-school boys to confront Pascal, Pascal who had hardly any schooling. He knew only two of the five words the boys gave him and they were therefore proclaimed the victors.

Then Pascal gave the high-school boys two words they did not know, added ten others, and two more for good measure, words like troglodyte, sebaceous, asininity, phlebotomy. They could not give the definitions of any of them, so the triumph was Pascal's, after all, and the high-school boys and Pascal parted, much pleased with each other and as admiring friends.

Pascal learned of public libraries and went to borrow many books. He felt very grateful to all librarians, for they were always kind and thoughtful and patient although his English was broken and his clothes were dirty and worn.

He was eager to learn the English language so that he might be able to express himself as an American, but that was not the only reason for his interest. He felt that most people did not understand laborers' lives, did not know what it is like to be a pick-and-shovel man. They could not appreciate the endless labor and hardship that has gone into the building of the many highways and railroads. He wanted to do something to help people be less ignorant and more thoughtful.

Pascal believed he had the ability to become a writer and he decided that somehow he was going to be one. An accident happened in a coal dump. A laborer was killed. Pascal wanted to be able to write so well that people would not only know about the accident but would feel how sad it was, would really feel how bad it was to care more about saving money than about making working places safe for working people.

A man sat grief-stricken at night before the shanty. The boss had told him he had grown too slow with pick and shovel, that he was too old now to work for him and need not come any more. Now there was no job and no money to live on. He had worked hard all his years but he had never earned enough to be able to save anything for old age. Pascal wanted to be able to write so that comfortable people might know how it felt to have no money for times of sickness and no money for old age. Perhaps then they would help change things.

And Pascal was a poet at heart who saw much beauty in the world. He had a great desire to be able to tell of the gladness in his soul when he had seen a bush of acacia in bloom beside a working-man's shanty.

He dreamed and dreamed and wished and wished he might be a writer and worked toward that end in his free time. One day he decided he had done enough of wishing, and of putting only odd moments of time on his ambition. Now he would set about being a writer in earnest, give all the hours of the day and evening to it.

He acted quickly, before his plan might seem too daring and he might change his mind. He went to his friend Saverio. "Saverio," he announced, "I am going to leave this place. I am going to live in the city and write poetry."

"Pascal," Saverio answered, "you will starve." "All right," said Pascal, "then I shall. I'm starving anyway, I'd rather starve pursuing the great gift of poetry." The next day he left the box car and the ditches and tracks.

One of the first poems he wrote in the city began,

"We who were born through the love of God must die through the hatred of Man." When it was finished, and a number of others he had long been thinking about had been written, he tried to sell them, but in vain. The editors always sent them back to him. Presently his money had given out. He took a job in a shipyard to earn his bread and butter. But he was restless. He felt he was meant to be a poet and that he must be one.

Because the rent was very low, he engaged in Brooklyn for a home an old shed room that had once been a chicken coop and wood shack. Stale bread and the cheapest, almost rotten bananas, of which he bought twenty-five for a nickel, he chose for his food, so that he might live as long as possible on the very little money he had. All day he spent writing, writing, and reading in the public library, working to be able to tell what he had to say.

When he had written a number of poems that truly expressed his feelings and thoughts, he began to trudge from one magazine office to the next, trying to sell them. Always he was told by the editors that they had all the poetry they wanted. But he did not give up trying to publish what he had written.

His overcoat was wrinkled and worn from years

119

of use as a coat by day and bed-cover by night. And his suit could not remember that it had ever been new. He became so poor that he had not even bananas and stale bread left, and his shed was so cold and damp that it seemed worse than outdoors. He almost despaired, but not quite. "There must be some way, there must be some way," he said to himself.

One day Pascal read about a poetry contest. He sent some poems to the editor, who read what Pascal had written. Pascal's long practice was showing. The editor became excited, very much excited, as anyone does who loves good writing, when he discovers something very good.

"These poems are beautiful," the editor said, "very beautiful indeed. They feel like a fresh breeze blowing through this office, among all the stale things that try to be poetry and cannot be that." And he printed them in his magazine.

Of course Pascal was as happy as could be. His poems were so well liked by the people who read the magazine that all at once Pascal found himself a noted person. Other magazines wanted more poems and people wanted stories about his life. His picture with pick and shovel appeared in the papers, labelled the "pick-and-shovel poet," and he received letters of appreciation from all over America. People wanted to tell him how greatly they admired a boy who had not permitted poverty, nor lack of schooling nor ignorance of the language to prevent him from learning to express what he had to say.

All this recognition gave Pascal much pleasure, but most dear to his heart were the tributes of his fellow workers, the toilers in ditches and mines and factories, who rejoiced that at last one of their number had learned to tell their feelings and longings to the world outside.

When some day the lot of the laborers and their families will be more free from grinding care, Pascal d'Angelo will have thanks for his perseverance, for he will have the right to feel that he had a share in helping the world understand the laborer's life.

SINGING HIMSELF FREE

THREE young negro lads and their mother were trudging the dusty road from Curryville, Georgia, to Chattanooga, Tennessee, each carrying as big a bundle as strength permitted. In Georgia they had been farmers, tilling a little ten-acre patch of ground which had been given the father and mother when they were freed from slavery.

The invalid father had died and now they were leaving because the mother did not want her boys to grow up ignorant. Curryville provided very, very little schooling, and Chattanooga promised a better education and a better living. The mother had sold the cow and the horse and the crop, and then, with what money they owned in their pockets, their household goods on their backs, they had taken the road. The mother was somewhat anxious, but the boys were only eager for the adventure of establishing a new home in a new place.

One of the brothers, the middle one, was Roland, Roland Hayes whom we now know as the great singer, then only fifteen years old. When they came to Chattanooga, Roland secured a job in a window-weight factory, where it was his work to carry great dippers full of molten metal to be poured into molds.

His feet became peppered with scars from the hot iron that spilled out of the dippers, but Roland liked his work and he did so well in the factory that after a time he was made foreman.

It had been the mother's plan that Roland's younger brother should go to school all the time, and that the other two boys, Roland and the oldest brother, should take turn about, working to make a living for the family and going to school. The boys, too, thought that a good plan, but it did not work out just so.

Because Roland's good earnings helped the family so much he did not return to school when his turn came to go, but instead attended night classes while working in the factory by day.

Now, Roland was a full-fledged factory foreman, but he was not only that. He was a singer, too, although he did not think of himself as such. He was always singing at his work. That was really against the rules but the manager liked having him do it because all the workmen enjoyed so much hearing him. His singing "kept the factory going," the manager said.

Roland joined the church and sang in the choir, but it had not yet occurred to him that he had any special talent. "I just sang," he tells, "because it was as natural to me as breathing. I liked to sing. All my people do."

One day he sang a solo in the church and that was a day he never forgot. It was so exciting to hear his own voice sound forth all alone, to see how proud his mother was, and how pleased his young musician-friend, Arthur Calhoun!

The mother became quite angry with that friend after the concert, when he dared suggest that Roland should have his voice trained. "Don't you dare put such notions into my son's head," she said.

She was very proud of the foreman's job he held, with wages better than many older men ever received, and she had never heard of a negro making his living with music except in dance halls. "I don't want any son of mine to take up that kind of life," she said.

For quite a while Roland took singing lessons from Calhoun, but he was not greatly interested

124

until one evening his teacher-friend had an inspiration. He took him to a friend's home to hear on the victrola some of the world's great singers, Caruso, Sembrich, Emma Eames.

Something happened to Roland Hayes as he listened. For the first time in his life he realized how wonderful music might be, what it might mean to be able to sing as these great artists sang.

"That night I was born again," he says. "It was as if a bell had been struck, that rang in my heart, and it has never ceased to ring there! I had not known what my friend meant when he talked of music. I had not been capable of imagining it!"

Then he knew he was meant to achieve something to which he could not attain as foreman in the factory, something with his voice. "I learned I had been put into this world to achieve some great purpose," he said.

It took him several months to make his plans. Then, with his mother's consent gained, and with fifty dollars, his share of the family earnings in his pocket, he set out, again journeying on foot for an education, this time in college.

When he came to Fiske University he was put on probation because he could qualify for the sixth grade only. But he made two grades in one year, besides earning his board and lodging, and of course then the school authorities were very glad to have him stay.

One day, about four years after he had entered the university, Roland Hayes went to Boston with the Fiske singers. There it came about through Mr. Putnam, who had been impressed with Roland's voice when he had heard him on a visit in the South, that arrangements were made whereby Arthur Hubbard, one of the greatest voice teachers in America, took the young singer as his pupil.

Roland Hayes was very grateful that this could be, but not surprised, for always, he says, things worked out in his life so that they served the great purpose he had come to believe in. Working out his life purpose, whatever that might develop to be, was not easy. While studying in Boston he had to earn enough money to pay for his board and room and his lessons. For a while he was bellhop in a hotel, then messenger in a large insurance office.

After the sons had gone their several ways the mother was left alone in her home in Chattanooga. Her son Roland could not endure the thought of his mother's loneliness, so he went home, helped her pack the household goods and sell the furniture, then he brought her back to Boston to live with him.

He found a cheap little apartment in which they set up a home. Out of the packing-box in which their goods had come Roland made a bed for his mother. He bought other empty boxes and fashioned out of them a table and some chairs and a bed for himself. The only piece of furniture he bought was a cook stove.

Keeping house on a seven-dollar-a-week messenger fee was a difficult task, but Roland and his mother managed somehow,—in time more easily, for the son began to earn small fees for singing at church concerts and at funerals.

For eight years Roland Hayes had studied in Boston, working very hard with his voice, learning languages, French, Italian, German, and studying the literature of song. He had tried himself out in several small concerts when he decided upon a great adventure. He would launch his career as a singer by giving a big concert, a concert in the great hall of the Symphony Orchestra of Boston.

When his plans became known he received some excited letters. How could he risk such an undertaking? his friends asked. Did he not realize that

127

the sum of $800 had to be guaranteed as rent for the hall? How could he think of promising so large an amount of money in advance? Did he know that no negro had ever given a concert in that building? What made him think people would come at all?

But Roland Hayes was working out his life purpose and he went ahead with his plans. He secured from Mr. Hubbard the names of interested people but also consulted a Boston telephone directory. Of course, a telephone directory does not tell which people on its lists love music, and it did not give Roland Hayes any such information. But he marked in it all the names that sounded good to him, and in his spare moments, on a battered old typewriter he had acquired, he wrote some 2,000 invitations to his concert. It was hard to save enough money for all that postage, but in due time the letters were sent.

Soon he found that his faith in himself and in the people of the city was justified. Each day tickets, and more tickets, were ordered. Enough were sold two weeks in advance of the concert to permit paying the $800 deposit for the rent of the hall.

On the evening of the concert so many people, negro and white, came to hear the young artist that as many as 700 had to be turned away. Musically as well as financially the affair was a great success.

Since then Roland Hayes has sung before the King and Queen of England and in all the countries of Europe and has delighted huge crowds in the cities and towns all over the United States.

One evening after a concert a man said to Roland Hayes, "I have heard all the famous singers. When I listen to you I get the same things which I get from their singing, but I also get something more, what is it?"

The young artist was made thoughtful by that question. "Is there really something in my singing that is different? If so, is it possibly something that is there because I am a negro? Have we negroes some gift of music, of understanding, of feeling, that is especially ours?"

The more he thought about it the more he felt sure that now he knew the purpose of his life. He said, "I will help my people use what has been given them, to make a special contribution, only a humble one, perhaps, but our very own, to human experience."

Everywhere, enthusiastic over his extraordinarily beautiful voice, over the superb way in which he sings in German and French and Italian and English the songs of many nations, over his interpretation of the negro spirituals, people, negro and white, say to themselves, "Evidently a negro can be as great an artist as anyone."

And so Roland Hayes' purpose is being realized; negroes who had been shy because they had been downtrodden have been helped to be very proud of their race and of their own gift to humanity, of song, of deep feeling, of rhythm and sound expressing their own understanding and emotions.

His mother died after the son had become a recognized singer. She had seen him acknowledged a great musician and recognized the equal of any artist of any color.

THE CHURCH'S BIRTHDAY

THERE was not always a Christian Church, although its history is old. Its birthday was one Pentecost Day, the first Christian Pentecost Day, and this is the story of its beginning:

After Jesus' death on the cross the hearts of the disciples, as one might guess, were full of deep sadness and mourning. Peter and Andrew, and James and John, and all the others, could think of nothing else but of all the suffering in the last days of Jesus' life, of his death and of the death of all their hopes for a future with him.

They would meet in the home of one or the other of his followers and gather what comfort they could from talking about him, from reminding each other of things that had happened in their life together with Jesus, from mourning together that the wonder of his presence was gone from them.

Then a very strange and wonderful thing happened. Jesus' presence became real to Peter and to John and to the others in such a way that they knew,

"He is not dead but alive." Their sorrow turned into a great joy that changed their lives. They began to discover how great a place was theirs to fill in the world as followers of Jesus, taught by Jesus himself.

"How could we spend so long a time only sorrowing?" they wondered now. "Better than any other people we know him, we who have seen his life among the people and his life with God. Now we must teach those who have not seen him that they too may know him."

"Did he not tell us," they reminded one another, "that in God's strength we would be witnesses for him in 'Jerusalem and in all Judea and in Samaria and in the uttermost parts of the earth'?" They remembered those words with gladness, for there was nothing they would rather do than tell people about him who meant so much to them.

They still met together regularly to pray and to talk with each other about all the things that happened in their life with Jesus while he was on earth, and about all he had meant to them then and since, but now their hearts were full of hope.

They were beginning to see that Jesus' plans for the establishment of the Kingdom of God did not end with his death. "Go ye into all the world," he had commanded them, "and make disciples of all the nations."

On one great holiday, the feast of Pentecost, when again the disciples had been praying together, the glory of their task dawned upon them in its fullness and the spirit of the Lord possessed them. They went out among the holiday crowds in the temple courts so serenely happy that the change was a marvel to those who knew them.

Peter felt that he must preach the gospel of Jesus to the great throng gathered for the celebration in the courts of the temple. He stood forth on the porch, with the disciples and other friends about him, and preached a sermon. It was a wonderful sermon, one that seemed to make Peter's own love for his master contagious. Three thousand of the throng that heard him said to themselves and to one another, "We want to be followers of that great Jesus too," and let themselves be baptized in his name.

That is how the first Christian congregation began. The members of this first congregation did not yet think of their group as a church, but that is what it really was. The people who had promised to be followers of Jesus met regularly to pray together, to learn together about being children of God, and about living and thinking after Jesus. No one said of anything he had that it was his own; everything each one owned, all his possessions, he shared with all the rest, so that there might be none among them in need.

More and more people joined the group and by and by there were so many that the disciples, now also known as apostles (that is, missionaries), could not do all the teaching and preaching and also care rightly for the widows and orphans, for the sick and for those in any other kind of need. Therefore they said to the members of the church, "Look about you for seven wise and honest men, men of good reputation and filled with the spirit of God, who may be appointed as helpers."

That suggestion pleased the congregation and they elected seven men whom they thought worthy of such trust. These seven knelt before the apostles, who laid their hands upon them in blessing and consecrated them to the work of helpers in the church.

The Bible says of the members of the congregation that they "dwelt together in gladness," and when, as it very soon happened, some of them were criticized and derided and even punished and imprisoned for being followers of Jesus, we are told they went "rejoicing that they were counted worthy to suffer shame for his name."

So began the Christian Church, in which people learn of the things Jesus taught, help each other lead the life in God's presence he led, try together to build a world where all people may live in his fellowship as God's children.

WHAT IT COST

ONE morning, in a school for war orphans in Czecho-Slovakia, the pupils were chatting excitedly as they began the day's activities. The building which was their home and school had been given to them through the American Junior Red Cross and the American children had sent money during the war to help buy food for the children of the country. Now there were plans afoot for some mission of friendship whereby the children of Czecho-Slovakia might express their thanks to the children of America.

"There are not so many things we can do to show our thanks to the children of America," suggested Jan. "It wasn't much of a list we made yesterday!" "There are so many more of them than there are of us!" mourned Sarko. "And that was rather nice for us," broke in Rosa. "Just think how much the Junior Red Cross did for us!"

"I wish we could all go over and sing for them," said Bettka, remembering the times they had sung in various places and on many occasions in her own country. "How could we?" laughed the others.

136

"That would cost very much money, and we haven't any!"

Just then the director of the school arrived. He was father, teacher, counsellor, all in one, and the children greeted him with great affection.

"I have good news for you," he told them. "The boys and girls of this school are to come to America with me."

The children's eyes shone with excitement. "That is," the director added, with a mischievous glint in his eye, "if you are willing." "Aren't we though!" they chorused, as they clapped their hands and laughed, just as he knew they would. Bettka looked about her as if to say, "Aha, my plan was not so bad after all!"

"A committee has chosen our school to give some thank-you concerts to the people of America," the director went on. "They are giving me the money to pay your way. We will sing some songs in our language, the old folk songs of our nation, for the American people will like to have us share the songs we love the best. And we will sing for them some of their country's songs to show them how much we appreciate America."

Of course, the boys and girls were happy over the

prospect of the journey. They set to work with a will to improve their singing of the Czecho-Slovakian songs they had always known, and to learn in English some American songs loved in all America. Sarko, young artist that he was, made a picture of them all as song-birds, perched in the rigging of a sailboat on the way to America, "Because we will sing our way," he said.

Doctor Bakule, their director, always loved helping them with their music, and his heart was in this new task too. "You cannot really sing the American songs," he said, "you cannot sing any songs, unless you understand, and really feel what you are singing. So, if we are to sing the American songs with understanding we must study much about America in these days."

"We do know quite a little about America," offered Mary. "We get letters from American children every month, and we write to them in our English class!"

"That helps a great deal," answered the director. "Tell me what your letters from there have been saying."

"There's a boy named Jack who writes to me," reported Michael. "The last time he told about a new

138

automobile his father had bought. Jack wrote how fast it goes, how big it is and how much it cost."

"My letter," said Jan, "told about a doll-house that Charles built for his sister. He did not tell so much about it except that it had eight rooms and was worth a hundred dollars."

The director asked, "Did any letters tell about 'America the Beautiful,' about the rivers and lakes and mountains and skies and sunsets, about the fields and prairies, and about the good people there?"

"No," said Rosa, "we have noticed the American children tell mostly about how much things cost and how big they are and they don't tell about things that don't cost anything, like mountains and people. Probably they think we know that the country is beautiful and the people good."

"Probably," assented the director, "but let me know when the next letters come and what they tell about."

When the next letters came the children brought them to their singing class. "They don't tell about 'O beautiful,'" they said, "and they don't tell about 'home of the brave.' It seems the American boys and girls think we know all about that."

"What do the letters tell about this time?" asked the director. 139

"Mine tells about an electric train John received on his birthday," reported Frantik. "John tells that it goes almost as fast as a real train, that it is the biggest toy train made, and that it cost his uncle a great deal of money."

"All about how big it is, how much it cost, and how fast it goes," mused the director. "But, of course," he said to the children, "all that is always interesting. We all like to see things that go fast, and we are interested in things that are big, and we wonder over things that cost much money. It is very natural that their letters should tell about such things. But songs are not about how big things are, how much they cost and how fast they go."

Then he showed them reproductions of paintings by American artists and photographs of American landscapes, and the children learned what "spacious skies" and "amber waves of grain" and "purple mountain majesties" in America might mean. He told them stories of American history, and they came to appreciate what the song means that tells of

". . . pilgrim feet,
Whose stern impassioned stress,
A thoroughfare of freedom beat,
Across the wilderness,"

140

and why the people of America love to sing "Away down south in Dixie." The negro spirituals charmed them, lovers of music that these children were.

They became so interested that they spent all their spare time in reading the history and literature of America. So these Czecho-Slovakian children learned of American pioneers and scientists and inventors, of artists, musicians and poets, of great men and women of the north and of the south, of the east and the west. They came to think so much of Abraham Lincoln that they celebrated his birthday in a special programme. And they grew very expectant of the beauty of our mountains and valleys and waters.

By and by the children were ready for the journey across the ocean, and they left for America with great eagerness for all that the experience might mean to them.

They came and gave their "thank-you" concerts in New York and Chicago, in Philadelphia, Washington, and Boston, and everywhere they captivated their audiences.

They sang humorous songs in their own language with such rollicking fun in their eyes and voices that all the audience laughed too, though they understood not a word. And when they sang their own national anthem, "Where is my home?" slowly and sadly, all hearers were sad with them, though they understood not a word.

Their voices were not lovelier than the voices of other children trained to sing, but their singing was more lovely than that of many children. When they sang "America the Beautiful," and "Land of the free and home of the brave," and "Mine eyes have seen the glory of the coming of the Lord," their songs touched the hearts of all hearers.

Some American people listening said to each other, "They sing our songs better than we have heard our own children sing them. How can that be? Why is that true?"

In one city the American school children gathered their nickels and dimes and bought some presents for the Czecho-Slovakian children. One gift was a reproduction of the statue of an Indian at prayer on his horse, which the visitors had admired in one of the parks of the city; the other was a camera, chosen because the visitors had been heard to say that they would like to take pictures of the many beautiful places they were seeing.

The statue was small, and the camera was no

larger than a traveller's camera ought to be. When the gifts were presented the American children appeared worried. They said, "These gifts are not very big, and they could not be so very costly, for they were bought with boys' and girls' nickels and dimes, which was all most of us had. We hope you will think them worth taking on your long journey home."

The visiting children thought that was a strange thing to say, when the spirit of friendship was so evident in the gifts. Who had ever heard of being concerned about the money cost of a gift received! And they thanked the American children very enthusiastically and sincerely for noticing and remembering the special desires they had expressed, and for getting so quickly the things they had most wanted. Then the Czecho-Slovakian children sang their farewell songs and prepared to sail for home.

For days after the visiting singers had gone, many people kept on humming to themselves over and over again the words and the music of "O beautiful for spacious skies" and "O beautiful for pilgrim feet," with the loveliness in its meaning that the Czecho-Slovakian choir had put there for them.

A MODERN PIED PIPER

ON a street curb in the city of Prague sat
Frantik, a boy of ten who had no arms,
one of the many war orphans in that Bo-
hemian city. People threw him pennies because
they liked the cheerful child and felt sorry for him,
but also because they were curious again and again
to see how he used his toes to pick up so adeptly the
coins tossed in his direction, and how he put them
into his pocket so neatly.

One day a stooped, black-clad man of about fifty,
with a big black sombrero on his head, passed Frantik's corner. He was a teacher of music and a
teacher of children. Tears started to his eyes as he
watched the boy. Somehow he knew that Frantik's
cheerfulness was a surface cheerfulness only, worn
because the boy was the good sport that he was.

"If you could be fed, and taught to work well,
would you be glad?" Doctor Bakule asked Frantik.
The boy smiled an answer that could not be mis-
taken, though his eyes were full of doubt that the
question could really mean anything as hopeful as its
sound.

DOCTOR BAKULE OF PRAGUE

"Do you like music?" The boy's eyes responded as if he had been asked if he liked to eat. "I sit at this corner," he answered, "because they have much music in that house over there. But I could never make music."

"Come, follow me, and we two will do as well at least as we have been doing in the past, for two are better than one alone, is it not so?" Then Frantik the boy followed Frantisek Bakule the teacher, as they went to the teacher's room, where the rent was paid for one week to come. And the teacher had five dollars in his pocket, which was all the money he had in the world.

Doctor Bakule taught Frantik to sing, and the boy had a lovely voice. In the course of the week several other waifs from among the hundreds of homeless children in the streets of Prague joined themselves to Frantik and Doctor Bakule, all spending their days learning to sing while also learning to carve toys and small trinkets to sell for a living.

The little band would go out to sing, rollicking, humorous songs and quaint sad ones, all sorts of songs. People enjoyed hearing them and paid them small money. The children accepted these earnings gladly, but they had another reason for their street

145

concerts. They wanted to interest other waifs in the school and home they were helping Doctor Bakule establish for them all, about which Doctor Bakule would give little talks after the singing.

Some of the little vagrants who came to listen scoffed at the enthusiasm of the group. How foolish to get excited over any kind of school! But others remained to join the singers. Doctor Bakule looked like a modern pied piper when he came along the streets, groups of children clinging to him and following after him.

The teacher's room was too small to house them all, and a big deserted barn on the outskirts of Prague became their home. They needed furniture, and since there was no money to buy it, the children and their teacher made what they required, chairs and work benches, interesting work benches that could be opened to provide beds for the night.

Doctor Bakule did not know how to make furniture, but he set out to learn, keeping just a lesson ahead of his pupils. They made flower sticks, too, and boxes and toys, carved, and decorated with colors. Each day they took account of their assets and always found that they had enough money to buy the food they needed for the next days.

146

The crippled children in the group, a score or more after a time, the little girl who had only three fingers, Frantik who had no arms, and the others, outgrew their feeling of being useless in the world. They learned to be independent, and more than that, they realized they could be of much use to others.

As the war progressed, and the crippled soldiers returned from the front, these children were very helpful in teaching the soldiers to use the limbs left them and in keeping up courage meanwhile. "If that armless young Frantik, if all those handicapped young children, can make life a courageous thing, surely we can too," the crippled soldiers would say to themselves.

One day a wealthy man offered them a hundred fifty thousand crowns, but the children voted not to accept the money. "Please give it to children who really need it," they said. "There are so many of them. The Ministry of Education will know how to use it for them." To such degree had their sense of independence grown. When someone offered to buy them better tools they were glad to accept the gift, so that their work might be more worthy.

As they sold more and more of their products they saw how much they needed to know arithmetic.

"There are only about a hundred number combinations," said their teacher. "Let us learn them," they said. And they set to work with such a will that in two weeks they had mastered the number combinations.

When Christmas was approaching the children who could write sent letters to relatives to tell them of their whereabouts, and many of them were invited to homes for the holidays. One boy, who had not wanted to learn writing, said to his teacher, "Will you write to my uncle for me?" "I will not write for you," said the teacher, "but I will gladly teach you how to write for yourself."

The boy put off learning and when he was finally able to write a letter it was too late. Doctor Bakule provided a lovely celebration but did no writing for him. So that boy, too, learned that one must not depend upon others for anything one should do oneself.

The children learned to be father, mother, brother, and sister to each other, and several volunteer teachers who came to assist Doctor Bakule helped the family spirit. The barn had given place to a huge army tent as a home and it looked like the home the children felt it to be. They had had a happy time decorating it, using their ever-growing artistic abilities.

People who observed the conduct of the school and noticed that there was no force, no punishment of the usual sort, asked, "What is your creed, by what philosophy do you work?"

"To live, to love, and to work are main points of our creed," said Doctor Bakule, "with praise to the good God for helping us, and prayer to him that we may be doing right."

Because he worked so differently from the educators of Austria, the people of the government thought of Doctor Bakule as a queer radical and agitator, and he had to work quietly to keep out of trouble. Then something happened that helped people to see what a wonderful school he had developed.

Summer time came and the children were invited to spend their vacation in a camp conducted by some people interested in children's welfare. It came to the notice of the leaders of the camp how much initiative certain of the children had, a number of them crippled.

It was they who made the marionette show and set it to work and gave entertainments with it, it was they who had the idea of printing a camp paper and who planned it and really wrote and printed it, it was they who thought of giving a play and knew how to go ahead about writing it, about designing setting and costumes, it was they who had such out-standing poise as players.

Then it was found that these children were the ones who had been taught by Doctor Bakule. A thoughtful woman who had visited the camp studied further Doctor Bakule's ways of teaching and the work he had done in helping homeless, handicapped vagrants become self-respecting citizens. She was so impressed that she told the government about it, and soon Doctor Bakule was hailed as a savior of the youth of his country.

The American Junior Red Cross became interested in the school. Through the Red Cross a gift of $25,-000 from a wealthy American was sent to Doctor Bakule so that the school might have a more per-manent and satisfactory home than the army tent.

Great was the joy of the children over this gift. In the big white building that became the home of the school it was possible to house many more, and more and more children were added to the group. Tonca came, a little sad and undernourished gypsy orphan. There was too, among others, Jaroslav, the boy thought by his people to be an idiot but who needed only a loving teacher to release his mind from the captivity his crippled body had put upon it.

The children, with their teachers, managed the growing household. One American visitor observed Rosa, the little girl with only three fingers, carving a box held before her in a vise, then coloring the finished work. He found the box so lovely that he asked to buy it. Rosa called Frantik, who was business manager. The boy figured the price, "slipped a foot out of his shoe," tells the visitor, "took our money in his toes so deftly that we scarcely noticed it, and slipped the money into his trousers pocket."

Doctor Bakule was asked, "But what do you get out of all this labor?" He smiled as he put his arm around ten-year-old Tonca, his gypsy daughter. "Why, isn't it enough for anyone to see this little girl with the bloom of health in her cheeks and happiness in her eyes and know one has had something to do with putting them there? What pay does anyone want for saving lives and making little children happy? That is my pay."

The visitor who had asked the question glanced over the group, saw the oldest of the children arrange, in motherly fashion, the disordered costume of the youngest, heard some boys discussing what they would do when they grew up because that would be "best for our country," and he knew that all the nation would be happier through Doctor Bakule's way of making children happy.

NOTES

The brief notes which follow will lend interest to the telling of these stories:

> *His Honor, the Judge.*
> *Consequences.*
> *A Surprise Package.*
> *The Church's Birthday.*
> *What It Cost.*
> *A Modern Pied Piper.*

NOTES

HIS HONOR, THE JUDGE   page 1
CONSEQUENCES   page 10

The setting is in the city of Detroit, in the years indicated. The Ford Republic is a "Boy Community," a farm school for boys who have been judged "delinquent" by the Wayne County Juvenile Court. It is maintained by a group of citizens who believe that exercise in self-government and in self-restraint may make boys into reliable citizens while forced discipline, such as is prevalent in the ordinary "reform school," will make them merely resentful of government.

In the Ford Republic there are no rules that have not been voted upon and accepted by the boys themselves; no one watches the boys and makes them work or go to school, but every week every citizen must pay his board and laundry and clothing. When a boy goes to school regularly and does his share of the farm work he can easily earn what he needs and money for "extras" besides. If he loafs and has not enough money at the end of the week to pay his board he is brought into court and reprimanded for letting the citizens' taxes pay his "keep." Then he is put on State Labor, has to work harder than the free boys, and without pay.

All of the first story is historical, constituted of facts and incidents learned chiefly through the kind offices of Mr. Fred Butzel of Detroit, member of the board of managers of the school and friend of Fred Bloman. The second story is based upon an incident in the history of Fred Bloman's tenure of office.

A SURPRISE PACKAGE   page 39

The story of Commander John Rodgers' flight belongs to the aeronautical history of the year 1925. That the giant seaplane he was commanding was forced down only fifty miles from the next refuelling ship, and found after nine days of finally almost hopeless search, is a matter of well-known record. It was also a matter of record that "between them (the ship-wrecked crew) and one of the most fearful deaths known to man, there remained only their courage and a small still for purifying seawater which had been brought along solely because of the insistence of the commander's mother." (*Literary Digest*, Sept. 26, 1925.) The other details in the story are imagined.

THE CHURCH'S BIRTHDAY   page 131

A story for telling on Pentecost Day, or on the day when new members are admitted into the church or when the elders or trustees are installed.

WHAT IT COST   page 136
A MODERN PIED PIPER   page 144

The impetus for the first story came through the author's attendance upon one of the concerts given by Doctor Bakule of Prague and his pupils while they were in America. The pupils of a public school in Boston presented the visiting singers, on this occasion, with a reproduction of Cyrus Dallin's statue, "Appeal to the Great Spirit," and with a camera. The story is imagined around this incident.

The second story, except for small details, is history. It is based upon the reports of visitors in Prague who studied there Doctor Bakule's experiment in education, visitors personally known to the author and those who have reported in print what they saw.

ACKNOWLEDGMENTS

Acknowledgment is gratefully made to the following publishers for permission to use certain material which has suggested some of the stories included in this book.

To Dodd, Mead & Company for *The Life of the White Ant* by Maurice Maeterlinck, and for *The Life of Jean Henri Fabre* by Abbé Augustin Fabre, as used in connection with *The Termites* and *What a Jingle Started*.

To Houghton Mifflin Company for *Jefferson and Hamilton* by Claude G. Bowers, as used in connection with *Hamilton and Jefferson*.

To John Day Company for *New Schools in the Old World* by Washburne and Stearns, as used in connection with *A Modern Pied Piper*.

To the Century Company (*St. Nicholas Magazine*) for *The Pied Piper of Prague* by Milton V. O'Connell, as used in connection with *A Modern Pied Piper*.

To the Macmillan Company for *Pierre Curie* by Marie Curie; *Pascal d'Angelo, Son of Italy* by Pascal d'Angelo; *On the Edge of the Primeval Forest* by Albert Schweitzer; *My Childhood and Youth* by Albert Schweitzer, as used in connection with *Pierre and Marie Curie; A Pick-and-Shovel Poet; A Zinc-Lined Piano*.

159

ACKNOWLEDGMENTS

To J. B. Lippincott Company for *Hawkers and Walkers in Early America* by Richardson Wright, as used in connection with *Blessed Are* . . .

To the Missionary Education Movement (*Everyland Magazine*) for *The Girl Who Won a Medal* by Susan Mendenhall, as used in connection with *For Margaret Knew.*

To Charles Scribner's Sons for *From Immigrant to Inventor* by Michael Pupin, as used in connection with *Michael's Acquaintances.*

To the Viking Press for *Portraits in Color* by Mary V. Ovington, as used in connection with *Singing Himself Free.*

To the Crowell Publishing Company (*The American Magazine*) for *A World Famous Singer Whose Parents Were Slaves* by Mary B. Mullett, as used in connection with *Singing Himself Free.*

The author is indebted to Houghton Mifflin Company for permission to use the lines on page v from *Abraham Lincoln, A Play* by John Drinkwater.